STRESS
RELIEF

STRESS RELIEF

Sharon Faelten & David Diamond

ADAPTED AND EDITED BY
Peter D.O'Neill, M.PHIL.

EBURY PRESS ■ LONDON

Published by Ebury Press
an imprint of Century Hutchinson Ltd.
Brookmount House
62–65 Chandos Place
Covent Garden
London WC2N 4NW

First impression 1989

British Library Cataloguing in Publication Data
Faelten, Sharon
  Stress relief.
  1. Man. Stress
  I. Title   II. Diamond, David   III. O'Neill, Peter D.
  155.9

  ISBN 0 85223 778 2 (Hardback)
  ISBN 0 85223 733 2 (Paperback)

Typeset from Editor's disk by Saxon Printing Limited, Derby

Printed and bound in Great Britain at The Bath Press, Avon

CONTENTS

INTRODUCTION

Taking Control

The city slicker and the farmer, the playboy millionaire and the unemployed angler, the woman QC and the homebound young mother, all seem worlds apart, yet stress comes to them in different forms, day and night. Working the land, working the system, not working at all – it seeems as though any and every lifestyle is filled with stress. The career woman envies her sister who stays at home with the baby, while the young mother wishes she could get out of the house and talk to grownups now and then. Everyone of us experiences a good amount of stress almost every day. Some people seeem to take it in their stride, while others are overwhelmed.

What accounts for the difference? What enables some individuals not only to cope but thrive in the face of trouble, while others crumble?

The answer seems to lie in the way we perceive a situation. Given the same set of circumstances, one person may see a crisis where another finds an invigorating challenge. The difference in perception may explain why an astronaut can step into outer space, while others are too afraid to step out onto the zebra crossing.

The key to controlling stress, the experts say, is learning to see things in a certain way. Suppose your job requires you to move to another city. It means you'll have to sell your home and buy a new one, leave your old friends and live among strangers, ease your children into a new environment, learn to do a new job while working for a new manager. Stressful? Absolutely!

But this stress can be handled. Let's view these circumstances as an exercise in perception. Think how would you feel if you had to sell the house and buy a new one? You may see it as a hassle, which it is, but you may also recognize it as as an opportunity to make a profit on your old home, allowing you to buy a better one. And yes, you will leave your old friends. But you know you'll make new ones. The children will become more mature and experienced, the new job will be a stimulating challenge.

Stress is an opportunity for growth and excitement if viewed in the proper perspective.

Here's another factor: People who successfully cope with stress are usually very committed to what they do. Some overriding goal or belief gives them purpose, a purpose that gets them through life's inevitable crises. What's more, stress-resistant people exert some control over their lives. They cope, not crumble, when a crisis such as illness hits. And they manage to keep internal stresses like guilt and worry in perspctive. You might call these factors the Three C's of stress management – Challenge, Commitment and Control.

This book is about learning to equip yourself with those three C's. You will soon find that the balance of this book is on the positive. It is not a book that hypochondriacs will find any room to wallow in. Those chapters that outline the problems are precise and usually short. The meat of the book lies in getting to grips with and solving your problem to reduce stress. The reader should take comfort in the fact that it has been researched against a background of eminent expertise in prevention in the United States by members of the staff of the Rodale Press *Prevention* Magazine who are listed at the back of this book. In this Ebury edition we have retained many of the American sources that were used in the US edition because their views are part of the international debate about stress reduction and the quality of life. They stand valid in that debate. It also reflects an awareness of the need for a new partnership between those with chronic problems of stress and the medical profession.

This book is not a substitute for expert medical help and wherever you are in doubt you should consult your doctor. But at the same time this new partnership should mean that there is far more to that medical help than popping a pill. It will be all the more successful when doctor and patient understand, not only each other, but how best to tackle the common problem they face.

This book opens the door to a happier, healthier, more satisfying life. Enjoy reading it and finding out a great deal more about yourself than you ever thought possible.

1

HANDLING EVERYDAY HASSLES

Boredom ■ Cars ■ Commuting ■ Competition

Deadlines ■ Dieting ■ Disappointments

Dual-Career and Single-Parent Households

Executive Stress ■ Family Feuds

Holidays ■ Travel Planning ■ Loneliness

Stage Fright ■ Workaholism

BOREDOM

Are you eating everything in sight or nothing at all? Are you still struggling to get to sleep in the middle of the night and waking up at the crack of dawn, or can't you drag your head off the pillow? Is your mind a blank or a maelstrom of ideas? Do you snap at the people you live with, take stupid risks and have lots of little mishaps?

If you answered 'yes' to any of the above then you may simply be suffering from a case of boredom which has turned you into a manic or a zombie. Psychologists now suggest that being understimulated by the daily challenges we meet in life can result in various psychological and physical effects. Most of what we read about stress focuses on the overload. But Dr Augustin de la Pena at Texas University says '... the *underload* side of stress in adults is the predominant side. In other words you are bored because you do not have the necessary minimum, normal amount of stress the body needs to function.

The Manic Zombie

Paradoxically, while we grow and our brains gain the capacity to process ever-increasing amounts of information, when we are bored the brain goes on autopilot and starts trying to compensate by sending out signals to increase the input of, or sensitivity to, information. Dr de la Pena suggests that this explains why what excited us as children bores us as adults. And when we try to regain that fun and interest we may end up on the overload side.

Uncontrolled, this brain activity may increase the possibility of illness or a feeling of illness, back pain, high blood pressure, certain cancers, some eating disorders, and create other problems, according to de la Pena. His research shows that the chronically bored brain pursues stimulation by causing increased Rapid Eye Movement (REM) or 'dreaming' sleep. The more you are bored the quicker you get into REM sleep.

But since the REM sleep signals the brain to wake up, the bored wake up earlier than they want. Here is what you can do to tackle this state. First make sure that boredom is the cause, then try some of these steps:

■ The degree of boredom can be gauged by making a list of what stimulates you and then score them on a scale of one to ten. It is important that you do this for yourself or you will not be motivated to follow it up. Secondly different people need different stimuli – preparing a Chinese meal for the beans-on-toast addict will have the same effect as going to the cinema for someone who only reads books and never watches television. Specific activities should also have an immediate effect.

■ Systematically build up a series of challenges during your working and social day, but don't overdo them.

At work:

■ Look for the signs in yourself (you may think it is only others who are affected), such as loss of attention, irritability, staying off work, or, *in extremis,* a feeling of helpless incompetence where you feel you cannot get anything done.

■ If you are in a big organization see if they offer refresher courses which include aptitude tests. You can always say that you are looking for a new challenge whether it is getting out of the desk force into the sales force or off the assembly production line into quality control. Some people in desk jobs may also find it worth spending a spell on the shopfloor. It may not only be productively satisfying, there can be a great deal of open friendship there away from the office politics. (See Index, Executive Stress)

■ Don't hesitate to ask for more responsibility but work out exactly what it could be.

■ If you have to keep a low profile or you work in a small outfit, get your trade union or staff representative to suggest to management the purchase of a Work Stress Management Package, or brochures on healthy mental health at work. (See Reference List, Living Skills, Mental Health at Work)

In your social life:

■ If you want to keep your increased activities outside your boring daily work, take an evening job or hobby, or voluntary work.

■ Diversify: If you're a domino player then stretch yourself to chess. Cut down on the television and start playing the piano.

■ Don't just look at the holiday brochures – read a guidebook or learn the language

■ Meditation (See Index) is a good way to learn how to control your state of mind and be aware of how your mind and body are ticking over through biofeedback. (See Index)

■ Don't: Overdo it, Drink, Eat or Drug yourself to relieve your boredom. You may end with something worse, particularly if you OD!

The People Who Bore you

Dr Mark Leary, of Wake Forest University, is America's leading specialist in bores. He says the worst are those who complain about themselves and their lives, as well as people who can only deal in inanities. After them come the people who use too much slang or jargon or try too hard to be nice. These are people, Dr Leary says, who get in the way of real communication. We would all like to have the same rewards from our relationships as we get from our jobs. But it is easier sometimes to modify or change a boring job.

You can help make life less boring for people:

■ Get them to relate to other people, sometimes by stealth.

■ Try to discuss interesting things with them, particularly when others are present. Don't huddle endlessly over how the silly mid-on kept dropping balls after a maiden over.

■ Avoid being boring yourself. Agree on a signal with your partner so you can each tell the other when you are boring a third party out of their minds.

CARS

Which is the most annoying kind of delay: a traffic jam, a train stopped for no apparent reason, or getting off a plane? They are all as bad as each other, depending on your state of mind. The key to them all is feeling in control of your situation.

Car Cares

Cars can cause you stress, especially if you have bought one beyond your means and you are constantly worried about the repayments. Next time buy a cheaper one. You could decide on a second-hand car with a reliable guarantee. This allows you not only the opportunity to buy a bigger, more comfortable car, the cheaper price will certainly offset the extra petrol cost, and probably reduce the insurance premium. But work out all the running costs as well as the purchase price. Look at the consumer magazines. Budget ten per cent extra of the purchase price for unexpected problems.

Some ways of coping with cars:

■ Join a national breakdown organization; apart from the

13

peace of mind, it could save you a lot of money if you break down in the middle of nowhere.

■ Make sure your vehicle is well maintained. If you cannot afford to pay a garage then learn to do the basics, such as changing the oil regularly. Change the fan belt when you have a service even if they tell you it is not necessary. It only costs a small amount extra. Have the brakes checked on a fixed day each year or according to the mileometer. A stitch in time really will save nine. Winter, summer and holiday trips all need some preparation. Keep a survival kit in the boot. That can mean something as simple as a bottle of water for the radiator and a spare can of petrol.

■ Think about a car share. Schemes available like that of Green Cars (See Reference List) in the UK offer you a model agreement on how to do it. Their research shows that there is usually very little conflict between users. Where there are, say, four households, they can afford a banger, a big long-distance car and a minibus between them. It cuts your running and maintenance costs dramatically, and on the rare occasion when you are without a vehicle there is always a taxi, a train, a bicycle or a bus.

■ If you are status-conscious and drive up in a cheaper car to a wedding reception, just tell people your Jag has been borrowed by your father-in-law.

On the Road

Once you are behind the steering wheel you will inevitably encounter stressful driving. Tackle the situation with these strategies:

■ If you are caught in a traffic jam and do not have a car phone to swing your latest deal on then listen to the radio and sing. Traffic jams are 'opportunity time' to do a little planning or meditating.

■ A car phone could keep you occupied, but it may also steal your mental free time in the car. You can always switch it off, of course.

■ Think about joining a car pool.

■ If you deliberately resist fighting someone over the fast lane or moving an extra three yards in a traffic jam, that should make you feel better, if not superior.

■ Stagger your arrival and departure from work with flexitime. So long as everyone knows you are putting in your hours, there is no guilt or recrimination attached to this.

COMMUTING

Other strategies have to be employed to tackle the tension when you travel by train. The fact that a delayed train is beyond one's control, makes it even more vexing and affects even the least aggressive of people.

■ If you leave a little earlier or towards the end of the rush you may be able to sit, instead of stand, all the way to work.

■ It may be enough for you to read or catch up on work on the train. But commuter groups can be very successful, not only to improve your contacts, but your bridge or holiday languages. Some train groups even pay for occasional lecturers.

■ Some US rail authorities have had the imagination to install a library service on the train and it is much appreciated by those who get home too late to get to their local library.

■ Sleep. Surveys show that a lot of people sleep or snooze on train journeys. In fact sleep is a natural part of our time clock which the nine-to-five job syndrome has destroyed. So go to sleep on purpose without begrudging yourself. A neighbour can be asked to make sure you do not sleep through your stop.

COMPETITION

All of us know that there is more to life than the rat race, that competitive lives are lives dictated by stress, but most of us are unable to do much about it. What can we do to put competition in its proper perspective so that our workplaces are not scenes of conflict and our friendships not soured by undeclared contest?

One way to start is to ask oneself, 'What is really at stake? What is the worst thing that could happen if I lose?' Or investigate your own competitive impulses. That involves understanding what kind of competitors we are, why we compete and what is at stake when we do.

Our competitive behaviour often has its roots in childhood and the instinct for self-preservation. The patterns of competition we learnt then are revived in the other 'family', the workplace. And of course we may encounter employers who often deliberately pit employee against employee in the hope of improving everyone's performance!

Keeping Up is Hard to Do

Among the most irksome forms of competition is that of status, measured by the number of possessions. The latest piece of electronic wizardry, the sports car or the swimming pool are often acquired not because we *need* them, but because they signal 'RICH, RICH, RICH' to the Joneses. Then we can only hope that they don't buy something in return which says 'RICHER, RICHER, RICHER'.

Such a game can be stressful, frustrating and *expensive* to maintain. You must question your attitudes and learn to realize that sometimes there is no real value in competition. Another person's gain is not necessarily your loss.

A more balanced perspective will also show you that there are other rewards than material success — like having and keeping your friends. So count your own blessings and seek your rewards, and don't worry about keeping up with the Joneses.

Working At It

At its harshest, competition in the office or workplace, in the boardroom or on the assembly line, creates basic fears over survival. For those who do not want to compete or who feel uncomfortable in such an atmosphere the wisest move possibly is to get out before too much damage is done. Even if you survive the job, it might affect your health. Working in an atmosphere which is tension-ridden can lead to constant and high levels of stress and this is certainly related to causes of illness.

There is another course of action. Bow out of a competitive line of work if it does not suit your personality. But that, says organizational psychologist Robert Lefton, does not necessarily mean changing jobs. The tactic is to learn how to deal with and control competition rather than be shocked when you encounter it.

'Suppressing, smoothing over or avoiding can spin up to a very high degree of stress. Problem-solving is the most effective means of dealing with a disagreement. It can be distressful up-front, but the long-term results are good,' he says.

So if you frequently find yourself arguing with someone at work you could:

■ Confront that person in a negative win/lose manner, warning that, 'if you try to get me, I'll get you'.

■ Smooth it over saying, 'well, we argue, but its really not *that* significant.'

■ State your concern openly saying, 'I'm very upset and

17

concerned about our constant arguing. Because of this our discussions deteriorate and our work suffers. What can we do to solve the problem?'

The first two responses will not help to reduce stress. While the first is a declaration of war, the second just submerges the tension and feelings of distress. But the third, which may involve facing confrontation, and demand courage and assertiveness can, in the long term, be more productive and actually save a great deal of stress.

Keeping your Friends

Competition plays an awkward and sometimes destructive role in friendships. Psychologist Lillian Rubin says that in male friendship, the competitive thrust is overt and direct; with women, its hidden from view, too often covered with a smile, a veneer of warmth and friendliness that bodes ill for the kind of trust a friendship requires.

The bottom line is that most men, because they are openly competitive, have difficulty forming intimate friendships. But when they are able to do so there is a strong undercurrent of affection beneath the competitive surface. Most women, because they are unwilling to acknowledge competition with friends, may destroy the intimate friendships they have. 'Women's inability to deal directly with competitive feelings is a source of difficulty in their relations with each other. For whether the motive is to compete or to avoid competition, it creates a similar distance between friends. You want to win, and you don't want to win.'

If you want to keep your friends and a possible competitive element of your relationship in perspective, acknowledge:

■ the fact that there is competition.

■ the feelings of jealousy and guilt.

■ the affection that exists between friends.

18

Mature and healthy relationships always include mixed feelings towards those we love. Maturity is a sign of having embraced and come to terms with these feelings that are a normal part of our experience. So, like the colleague at work, discuss them with your friend.

Of course it may be difficult to view the world in a non-competitive manner if the people you encounter are driven relentlessly by competition. But you can create a cooperative environment as a start and encourage similar responses.

It is really a matter of becoming secure in your relationships with your friends. This takes time, but it if you have thought about it sensibly, you will be able to gradually lower your guard towards your friends and be able to enjoy their company even more. Think of yourselves as being in the same team rather than on opposite sides.

DEADLINES

The television reporter who appears to have a hectic schedule, the accountant and the university lecturer who seem to have more leisurely working lives, are all bound by the discipline of the deadline. We have a limited amount of time to accomplish certain tasks, and irrespective of our profession, we all have to develop strategies to complete those tasks on time.

Dealing with deadlines to avoid stress is really a matter of setting up priorities, scheduling your time accordingly and making an effort to stick to both priorities and schedule. By doing this you gain control over your work and your life.

Be Realistic

'Many people are unrealistic about time. They either overestimate how long something will take or they underestimate,' says Californian psychologist Jane Burka. 'The first thing to do is to anticipate realistically how long a task will take and how much time you can spend on it. For instance if a project is due to be completed in a week and you're feeling optimistic

19

about that deadline, check your calendar. Are your in-laws coming to visit on one of those days? Do you have an all-day meeting another day?'

Even though you may have planned everything realistically, something unexpected could come along to rock your schedule. In such situations flexibility is your best ally. Develop the capacity to think quickly and be prepared for alternative action, to tailor your plans to cope with reduced time or a changed objective. This is what the news reporter has to do as the news stories come in – reassigning priorities and time devoted to the items. Plan in advance. Take action today to protect your time tomorrow. This may mean warning your colleagues or your secretary that you need to keep the morning of the next day free from interruptions. Once you've set aside time to work, be sure you have a clear idea of your priorities. Consider all the tasks you have and then list them in order of importance. You may find that the jobs lower down on the list were not terribly important anyway, or they were things you could not possibly have done, given your timetable.

The next stage is to assign priorities to your deadlines. 'Make up your mind which deadlines are really important and which ones are flexible,' says Dr Burka. 'On one hand you might want to finish reading a book by Friday, or you want to get a new job by Christmas. Those are self-imposed deadlines, which can be flexible. Then there are deadlines of real consequence – such as the last date for paying the car tax or finalizing the company accounts. These deadlines are inflexible. Meet them first.'

Step by Step

It will help if you view the task in hand as a series of specific steps. 'Rather than saying you have to have the quarterly report completed by Thursday and proceeding blindly, break down the project into very small and manageable tasks. For a six-page quarterly report, you might have to gather the financial data, talk to three people in your department, look at the last two years' worth of reports. Realistically assess the time required for each,' says Jane Burka.

To minimise the stress of a deadline, Dr Burka suggests you pick out the first step you can do in 15 minutes and do it. 'A person can stand almost anything for 15 minutes,' she says, 'and you may feel better that you're on your way to meeting your deadline. Then make a note about what you have to do next.'

Breaking up a project, making a deal with yourself to work only 15 minutes and rewarding yourself for completing a task are methods of seducing yourself into working toward your deadline. There are other techniques that delayers can employ. One American counselling psychologist says he simply turns on his computer. Then he reckons he might as well make a start on whatever he is supposed to be writing, because after all the computer is already switched on. If he has to do his taxes, he'll collect all the receipts. Then he'll say to himself, 'Now that I've got all the receipts together, I might as well sort them into categories.'

Such tips may be fine, but a person plagued by the tendency to delay should also look below the surface to understand the reasons why he or she has trouble meeting deadlines.

Some procrastinators take *every* deadline so seriously that they can't distinguish between those that are fixed and those that are flexible. Such people 'have to question their assumption that they are being judged by every challenge that they face. They need to realize that doing everything is impossible and that the stress of perfectionism is very costly,' says Dr Burka.

There are people who delay doing things out of rebellion, like not paying parking tickets or charges they consider unjust. Still others use procrastination as an excuse. Thus if they dawdle over a task and then don't do well they can blame the procrastination rather than their lack of ability. In essence they are protecting themselves from finding out if they would or wouldn't fail if they hadn't taken so long.

21

Deadlines are used by others to motivate themselves. They might do well at meeting the deadlines but they harm themselves by saying, 'I can only work well under pressure.' While this technique works well for some, it can result in ulcers, headaches and in drinking too much to deal with the stress of compressing work into a short span of time.

However, cramming may be best for some. Dr Robert Drabman divides most people into two groups in terms of how they accomplish tasks: plotters and crammers. Plotters chop off sections of work and proceed accordingly. Crammers wait until the last minute and work in a panic.

It makes sense to be a plotter, but says Dr Drabman, 'Lots of successful people function fine doing things at the last minute. Sometimes we try to be a way we are not, to be plotters instead of crammers, and that causes stress...the first thing you should do is whatever comes naturally to you. If what comes naturally doesn't work, if it provides stress, then you'll have to change.

'If you're a natural crammer, for instance, and you need the tension which cramming induces but you find your cramming is causing too much stress, you could at least set some sub-goals. That is, cram for parts of a project at a time.'

DIETING

We all know that stress can trigger the 'nervous munchies', but can dieting itself leave you tense, angry and frustrated? According to Dr Michael Lowe, who runs a weight management programme in Philadelphia, trying to lose weight is both physically and mentally stressful.

'The very fact that you are trying to lose weight implies dissatisfaction with your present shape,' says Dr Lowe. 'Being bombarded with image after image of ultra-thin, high-fashion role models can reinforce the feeling that no matter how much you diet, you're not going to be thin enough or attractive enough.

'The physical effects of dieting are stressful too, because evidence indicates that the body resists attempts to lose weight.' The very restriction on food creates a feeling of hunger which is stressful. There are many visual 'food cues' – restaurants, delicatessens, newspaper and magazine advertisements — all around us. 'Constantly saying no to desired foods leaves you frustrated, deprived and stressed.'

What can calorie counters do to avoid becoming a bundle of nerves? The following tips can counteract many of the feelings of resentment and deprivation that make weight control a torture to body, and soul.

■ Ask yourself if you *really* need to lose weight. 'Many people who are dissatisfied with their size aren't really overweight, but they're either on a diet or feel they should be,' says Dr Lowe. If you have good reason to feel fat – your weight is 20 per cent or more above that recommended for your height – then you need to face some facts.

■ Accept the fact that you will never be able to eat whatever you like, when you like, in any amount, without gaining weight. If you want to lose weight and keep it off you cannot expect to return to the eating habits of the past. Dr Lowe says he finds the people who ultimately adapt best to a dieting regime are those who can get past the feelings of anger and injustice and develop new feelings of pride at having overcome their 'handicap'.

■ Don't cut back drastically. A few weeks of strict discipline are usually followed by a return to old eating habits, leaving people feeling disgusted with themselves. Cut back gradually.

■ Don't embark on specialized or odd diets. 'Highly idiosyncratic diets that force you to eat only a few foods will also leave you feeling very deprived,' says Dr Lowe. You may become edgy and irritable and these diets are hard to follow once you are outside the home.

■ Allow yourself some indulgences. A black-and-white, all-

23

or-nothing approach can undermine the very thing you are trying to achieve. If you take such an approach, 'You are aiming for the impossible and setting yourself up for failure,' says Dr Lowe. 'So allow yourself an occasional stop for an ice cream cone, but don't keep a carton in the freezer.'

■ Congratulate yourself on the victories. If you are locked into a 'how much longer can I endure this?' attitude you will feel frustrated and angry, says Dr Lowe. 'If you focus on the healthy benefits of weight control, feelings of inferiority and deprivation give way to pride and your diet becomes a morale-booster.'

■ Plan ahead. On-the-spot decisions at meal times are of little use. Shop for food and plan your menus in advance. If you are going to a party, be prepared to decline an offer of something that does not fit in with your diet. Set a limit to how much you will eat, or eat sparingly earlier that day.

■ Don't let others coax or bully you off the diet. No-one, host or hostess included, has the right to pressurise you into eating or drinking something you shouldn't.

Losing weight is no piece of cake, but it doesn't have to be torture either.

DISAPPOINTMENTS

Consider the view from above. You are on the moon looking down at the earth. Somewhere below a man's blood pressure is rising. His nights are sleepless; he berates his wife and screams at his children. He cannot concentrate on his work and he takes no pleasure in recreation. The reason for all this stress? His new car is not what he thought it would be and it is a sore disappointment.

Of course buying a new car that turns out to be defective is galling. But, once again, consider the view from above. One dud car isn't going to mean much in the scheme of things. Ten years from now it won't matter at all. So why should you allow such a situation to interfere with your health and emotional wellbeing?

Disappointments do cause stress. It could be a minor let-down like buying an unsatisfactory electrical appliance, or a situation that matters a great deal to you – discovering you are infertile when you want very much to have children. But the difference between letting these setbacks destroy you and letting them challenge you is a simple matter of attitude, and of understanding what disappointments show us about how we view ourselves.

Working it Out

One situation that many people face at least once in their working lives is the trauma of not getting the anticipated promotion. When this happens it means someone is pointing out to you that you are not worth very much. You may then react by despising yourself. But ask yourself these questions: Should your self-image and self-respect be tied totally to a promotion and job prestige? Have you no worth, no reason to feel good about yourself except for this job?

In this case, as in most disappointments, the stress is basically a function of your own mind. It's not being passed over for the job, it's the meaning that you attach to it that causes the stress. Very seldom will the lack of a promotion mean a blow to the family in terms of finances. But it will mean a blow to the ego.

So if you're feeling totally put down by such a disappoint-ment, it's time for a little self-examination. People acquire their values from their parents and their peers, and they rarely question them objectively. This is what you must set out to do. Think about the way you view these things and your values. Is there an over-emphasis on job, status and prestige? If your values depend totally on external things such as advancement at work, the stress might never end because you might never advance enough for your own liking.

The chief element is the kind of message the person sends to himself about the disappointment. Saying to yourself, 'I must be a lousy person because I didn't get the job', is a pointless attribution of blame to oneself. In fact, work by several researchers has shown that people who tend to blame themselves for misfortune are more susceptible to disease. There is also evidence that self-blaming and other defeatist personalities create a self-fulfilling prophecy. You needn't make a catastrophe out of something that does not have to be one. Even those who experience something deeply disturbing, such as a loss of a child through a miscarriage, should remind themselves that the sad event does not mean they can never be happy again.

One common reaction is to say that life will never be satisfying again. If you say that to yourself, you make yourself feel worse than just the experience of the loss. You actually make the loss appear much deeper and heighten its effect. In fact a doom-and-gloom attitude makes it more difficult for you to climb out of your distress and get on top again.

How you respond to major disappointments can a have a profound impact on your life. Dr John Snarey, over several decades, studied how 52 young men, who had been diagnosed as infertile, coped with their situation. What he learnt could teach people a great deal about dealing with disappointments of this distressing nature.

Dr Snarey divided the men into three groups, according to the kind of 'replacement' they sought to deal with the stress of infertility. Members of one group treated themselves as their own babies, becoming preoccupied with, according to Dr Snarey, narcissistic activities such as body building. Another group of men seemed to find solace in objects, devoting themselves to a house, a car, a boat and the like. The third lot became involved in vicarious childrearing by taking an interest in the child of a relative, friend or neighbour.

By tracking the groups to midlife, Dr Snarey found that 80 per cent of those in the narcissistic group had been divorced and the remainder said they were unhappily married. In the substitute object category 50 per cent were happily married, 25 per cent unhappily married and 25 per cent divorced. In the third group, those that took an interest in someone else's child, 90 per cent reported being happily married.

For those who must cope with childlessness not of their choice, Dr Snarey says, 'Find important substitutes, other human beings. I would caution people not to focus on themselves.'

But finding a solution to a disappointment is not always easy. One strategy is to look for possible opportunities behind something that has gone wrong.

The following tips will help if, for example, you are going to buy a car:

■ Be realistic in your expectations. Anticipate that there will be some problems, but do not overrate them.

■ If you find that there are some things that are not quite right, rather than feeling stressed, create some form of control over the situation. Make a list of step-by-step actions. Write down what is wrong and when you want to take the car in for repair. Use this as an opportunity to employ your assertive skills.

This will help you take the stress out of your reactions. Don't blame yourself. And always consider the view from above.

DUAL-CAREER AND SINGLE-PARENT HOUSEHOLDS

John and Mary both have good jobs. He is a business executive and she is a teacher. This is what happens at home before they leave for work.

Ten-month-old William wakes up on a rainy Monday morning crying for attention at 7.15 instead of his usually dependable 6.30 a.m. Mary changes his nappy, furiously working to recapture the lost 45 minutes, and mentally rehearsing the assignment she will set her fourth-years in the first period at school. Eight-year-old Sarah, meanwhile, is telling her father that she thinks, just thinks, she has a sore throat, so could she have a hot drink and stay in bed another five minutes to decide? John in the bathroom is muttering about the wrong kind of razor having been bought; Mary in the kitchen uses one hand to feed William and the other to boil the kettle. From the bedroom Sarah is now ordering her breakfast and what she wants in her lunchbox; then she repeats the order as she races towards the locked bathroom.

John, trying to dress, has discovered that the suit to be picked up from the dry cleaners the day before, and needed for an important meeting, is still at the dry cleaners. He also finds that the crucial notes he had made for his 9 a.m. meeting are nowhere to be found.

Sarah is reluctant to brush her teeth, finds her cereal distasteful and cannot remember where her wellies are. Mary escapes from William for a two-minute shower and manages to make the 'wrong' kind of sandwich for Sarah while half wet and dressed in the kitchen. Mother and daughter face the prospect of seeing their usual bus disappear round the corner as they approach the stop. John makes do with another suit and finds his papers; but he has missed his customary commmuter train, and he will miss the next one – and God knows lose his job – if he cannot manoeuvre William into the car to drop him to the day centre and make it in time to the meeting. You can paradoxically multiply this by two in the single-parent family.

Finding Remedies

Allowing for some variations, hassled mornings like these are standard in families where both spouses work. 'People are more pressured in the morning,' says Dr Clifford Sager. 'When they are rushed in the morning they might not be thoughtful and, if they're annoyed at their mate, they can be spiteful. It's all very stressful.'

There is a host of relatively simple remedies for scenes of John-and-Mary-and-family madness. Here are some recommended by Dr Sager.

■ Use an alarm clock to wake you up. No-one in their right mind would depend on a baby.

■ If you have a single bathroom for the family, stagger the times of waking up so that there is an orderly procession in and out of the bathroom.

■ Prepare as much as possible of school lunches the night before. That also precludes a change of menu. Ask the children the night before what they want and make sure they stick to their choice.

■ Organize your clothes and those of your children before going to bed. An eight-year-old should be able to organize this, with only minor parental consultation. And if you've forgotten the dry cleaning or the launderette, then there is more time to take alternative action.

■ Set the breakfast table in advance as well. You could invest in a bedside teamaker to help you wake up.

■ To cope with offspring going in for the 'flu, make a small list of back-up people, whom the child knows well, who might be able to baby-sit during the day.

'The two most important things are advance planning and getting your children to be as independent and able to do as much as their ages and capabilities allow,' says Dr Sager.

It may seem quite natural to some that it is the woman's responsibility to smooth the passage from home to office and school. But with more and more women going out to work this has become an increasing cause of stress.

Housework

The only way one can defend housework is by comparing it to beating one's head against a wall – it feels so good when you stop. Of course you would like to keep a nice home, but you should not make yourself miserable over it. The key to cutting housework is to look at each chore and ask, 'How can this be prevented?'

A little ingenuity, shown in the following hints, can cut housework down to manageable levels.

■ Stop dirt in its tracks. Put down sturdy synthetic foot mats at strategic doors, to prevent dirt trailing in from outside. An extreme case would be the thick transparent runners used by builders when working in your house.

■ Keep your decor simple. Dusting around knick-knacks is tiring. Group them in one place, rather than scattering them around the room. Hang photographs and pictures on walls instead of placing them on tables.

■ Clutterproof your house. Keep to a minimum areas where this can accumulate. A hall table, for example, attracts bits like a magnet.

■ Create a control centre in each room. Keep shopping lists, mail, keys, on one shelf in the kitchen. Everyone will know where they are and it can be tidied up in one swoop. Stacking-bins for children's rooms are also handy.

■ Reorganize your kitchen. Store pans and most-used utensils within easy reach of work area – generally between the sink and the oven. This will save you darting about as you cook.

■ Tidy the toilet zone. Bath accessories and cosmetics often make a bathroom appear untidy. Keep these out of sight in a wall cupboard, or drawers; alternatively store them in atttractive boxes or containers. Use liquid soap and shower gel which eliminates soapy 'scum' at the wash basin and bath.

Home Help

Not everyone can afford extra help in the house, so make the best of the resources within the family.

■ Ask for help. Most family 'untidiers' are husbands and children. You could make each of them resoponsible for clearing their own mess. The major cleaning chores – the windows – could be tackled by arrangement with teenagers next door.

■ Share chores based on individual likes and dislikes. That way you will get the greatest amount of help from the family.

■ Decide where you can be flexible and where you will not compromise. If clean carpets and floors are your main concern, set that as a priority, but be ready to live with a little dust on the furniture!

Choosing Child Care

While financial pressures or pursuit of personal satisfaction may cause both partners to work, the single parent is generally under greater pressure. Society still offers little in the way of support, specially for people with pre-school age children.

Not enough companies offer day care for children of employees. Flexible working hours or job-sharing arrange-ments, once the hope of so many working mothers in particular, have generally been shunned by most employers. Places in nurseries and playgroups are not always easy to find and registered childminders are generally oversubscribed. So, depending on your resources, explore all the possibilities whether it means taking on an au pair, sharing a nanny or a baby-sitter, or an arrangement with a playgroup in the morning and a neighbour in the afternoon. If you are a single parent contact Gingerbread. (See Reference List)

Whatever arrangements you make – live-in help, a daily nanny, or a day centre – you will have the occasional twinge of

31

doubt when you wonder how your child is being looked after. Those nagging doubts can sometimes affect your work and your relationship with your child. Even parents who can afford the best care worry that they may be shortchanging their children. But part of the solution is to examine very closely how your child is being looked after, whether it is at a playgroup or with a nanny.

These are some of the issues you could consider:

■ What is the relationship between the childcare provider and the child? Do they care about the child. Do they pay attention to the child?

■ Think about the nature of the discipline your child receives. Is 'bad' behaviour treated as something to be stopped and punished, or as an opportunity to teach children how to solve problems, develop mutual respect and responsibility, and the ability to handle difficult situations?

■ Are children encouraged to talk, to think, to express themselves?

■ Is there enough staff to manage the children in small groups, so that there is good supervision?

■ Is the person who looks after your child trained for the job? Have they a sustained interest in their field – do they, for example, read about it?

■ Is there enough space? Are there enough interesting materials? Are these, and the activities, defined by age groups?

■ What is your relationship with the caregiver? Is it supportive? Does it make you feel guilty? Does the individual subtly make you feel terrible? ('Your child always behaves with me. I don't know why he cries with you.') Such comments can create conflict between the child and the important adults in his or her life.

Setting Priorities

Managing the stress of being part of a dual-career family is often a matter of using time efficiently, being organized, sharing responsibilities as a family, feeling comfortable about your childcare arrangements, and understanding your limitations.

The last of that list is especially important. The expectations you have of the relationship with your child can have a powerful influence. If you believe that all your time with your child should be 'quality' time, you are being unrealistic in your hopes and will be disappointed. No human relationship can be perfect all the way and there is a value to 'down' time.

Sharing Responsibilities

'Don't expect things in your household to be done as well as if that were your top priority,' says Dr Ross Webber, a professor of management at the Wharton School, University of Pennsylvania which has a prestigious international reputation. He recommends that you prepare yourself psychologically to lower your expectations, whether of the quality of your meals or the neatness of your child's room.

Dr Webber suggests you divide your time into segments. Pick two days a week for special meals, days when you know you'll be able to get home early or shop for food. 'The fact that you know you will have those two special meals will make you feel in control of at least part of the week and make you better able to deal with the fact that on other days you won't be having dinners like mother used to make,' he says.

Do the same thing for tidying your child's room. Pick one day to do it together. You'll know that it will be clean at least one day (or one hour) of the week and that may help you through the aggravation of the time when you know it is going to be in a mess. There is another benefit as well. Your daughter or son will view this experience positively, and may not be reluctant to do it when they are older.

If you think your house should be perfect all the time, think again. Doing things with your children is far more important than having a house with no dust. Many of our pre-occupations are actually cultural hang-overs.

Every dual-career household fits into one of four strategic frameworks, says Dr Webber.

■ Couples who put their career second to their own relationship or family. Those who believe in this tend to find it relatively easy to make time-sharing deals. The downside is that there could be adverse consequences for both careers and that, as the years march on, one partner may end up resenting the bargain.

■ Couples who agree that the husband's career comes first and the wife's is secondary. The wife bears the burden of running the home. Unfair as this might be, this arrangement appears to work best.

■ Couples who put the wife's career first and the husband's second. This is the most difficult to sustain because most men are conditioned to be the successful partner. They may become unhappy as they begin to see themselves falling behind their peers. This arrangement will probably work best if the man is not tied to an organization – he is self-employed, an artist or craftsman.

■ Couples who place their careers ahead of their own relationship or family. They have the slimmest chances of success for both their own careers and their relationship.

This analysis may make it easier for you in sharing responsibilities and managing time within, of course, the limitations imposed by your jobs. The simplest means of sharing chores is to have an arbitrary alternate daily or weekly schedule. But this does not allow for any great degree of flexibility in case one person's workload increases. If you alternate the chores according to how busy you are at work, you may be heading for conflict. Most successful couples work out a plan for sharing the household duties that match their needs and dispositions.

Accommodating Couples

The possibilities for dividing up work are reflected in the tasks shared by these four couples.

Jane and Matthew are teachers but they are also studying for postgraduate degrees. They have three children and they have established firm routines for their home life. They do not work on assumptions; each has a clearly defined set of tasks. Jane cooks and Matthew clears up. Matthew makes the breakfast with the help of their 11–year-old daughter while Jane gets the four-year-old ready for nursery school. Matthew cleans up after breakfast and cleans the house on Saturday mornings. Jane does the weekly washing.

Robert and Gayle have another method. She takes care of everything inside the house – the money, bills, repairs. He handles chores outside – the car, the roof and mowing the lawn. Because they both work shifts and odd hours, as a policeman and nurse, this arrangement suits them.

Sita is a teacher and Ramesh a freelance graphic designer. She likes to cook so she does all the meals, which she plans a week in advance. Ramesh, who often gets tired of being in the house, sees shopping as an opportunity to get out. They split the cleaning – she does the washing, he does the hoovering.

Sergio and Sue like to take turns with the chores but they do it on an ad hoc, daily basis. They have two pre-school children. Sue works for a local newspaper and has been able to negotiate a 24–hour week, working either all mornings or all afternoons. Sergio is in publishing and is able to bring work home. Sue cooks and cleans while Sergio works or looks after the two small children, or the other way around. With the two salaries they are able to pay for a part-time nanny for the children when Sue works afternoons.

Sue and Sergio are representative of couples who have established that family comes first, and career advancement second. Sue decided to reduce the number of hours she worked, and her salary as well, while the children are young. She even forfeited a promotion in the process.

Sharing Problems

What about the spouse who feels burdened by an unequal share of household chores and responsibilities? How does one get a partner to lend support?

Dr Bernard Guerney teaches people constructive strategies for dealing with such conflicts. These require skills that most people do not have.

One has to learn to see things from the other person's perspective. 'Most people only want to get their own point of view across and feel that to respect the other person's point of view would go against them. But the opposite is true,' says Dr Guerney.

He shows the wrong and the right way to approach the situation:

■ Wrong: I think you are a very inconsiderate person to have me do all the cooking all the time.

'You should be telling your partner what it is you want, and how you feel, in a way that's least likely to be threatening to the other person and most likely to make them want to cooperate,' says Dr Guerney. 'We teach people not to talk about the character or motives of the other person (you're very inconsiderate) which leads the partner to react defensively, nor to indulge in over-generalisation (all the cooking all the time) which invites counter-attack that this statement is not true.

And it usually causes the discussion to deteriorate.' By not telling the other person how you feel you make it hard for them to empathise with you.

■ Right: I'm feeling overwhelmed and very frustrated by the amount of work I'm obliged to do around the house, and I feel discouraged about the amount of help I get from you. You could be be a big help to me if you were willing to do some of these things.

After making such a statement, the next move is to stop talking and start listening to your spouse's reaction. Listen to his or her feelings.

"You want a constructive approach to problem-solving. So share your ideas, discover the basic issues, what you feel about them and what you want. Then you have to reach a solution where you get the most of what you want,' says Dr Guerney.

He believes that most people wait until the wrong moment to launch into their attack – when they can't take it any longer. They will be expressing negative emotions, crying or doing things that will put off the other person. 'Instead frustrated partners should discuss a problem before it becomes a hostile issue.'

Another common point of friction in a two-working-parent family is when a child falls sick. Ross Webber says that it is generally the wife who make the sacrifice and stays at home. 'When push comes to shove, her success or the risk of offending the organization is less than the man's.'

There is a Catch-22, says Dr Webber. A woman who asks for time off is usually treated more graciously by her employers than a man would be. So for her, taking a day's leave is less stressful. But in a way, her organization expects a woman to be less committed to her careeer. When she asks for time off to care for a child it may serve to strengthen the stereotype and the common conceptions of the commitment of a woman to her work.

If a man makes a similar request, the employer may be surprised. The boss may reason that if the man has not been able to organize someone to look after the sick child, how can he possibly be capable of managing the budget committee?

The solution to this dilemma lies in being prepared. Most people know the nature of their bosses. If one partner has a boss who is particularly difficult, then work out an emergency plan that will not require a day off for that spouse. This may mean having a list of people who can help (as sugggested earlier). But it is important that the decision on the day off is not taken unilaterally.

Pace Yourself

Making a move from harried employee to harried parent each evening is not fair to yourself, and certainly not fair to your children.

When you get home, stop for a moment to relax before rushing into your next bout of activity. This may take a bit of practice, but you'll find yourself better able to manage the stress of your busy lifestyle.

The Head of the Child Development Unit at Boston's Children's Hospital, Dr T. Berry Brazelton, says that it is important to save up some energy so that once you are home you will have enough for the children. Pacing yourself might mean not stretching yourself to the unnecessary extra mile for your employer, but the long-term benefits may well be worth it.

Dr Brazelton offers some other advice:

■ Compartmentalize. When you are at work, try to think about your work. When at home, think about what you're doing at home. Try not to bring work home from the office; try not to take your family worries into work.

■ When you get home, gather the kids up and be with them

38

as a family before you do anything else. If you have a baby, spend some time cuddling it, or if they are older just sit with them and spend some time talking to them. Then you can do the house work or prepare dinner. This tells them that you are all back together as a family, that you have time for them and that you are not still at work.

You can use a few other strategies to ease the transition from office to home. Find a few minutes of peace in exercise, meditation, a shower or bath, reading the newspaper, going through the mail to your favourite music or watching the news. If you use the bus, get off two stops earlier. The walk is a little exercise and it can act as a decompression chamber. If you are driving home, see if there is a park that you can stop off in for a ten-minute stroll.

In Tune With Yourselves
Keeping the household humming is one of the major objectives of a two-career family. The other is to keep the marriage itself in tune. There still are a host of stress-causing situations and reactions even if both partners have no problem with sharing the chores or organizing their childcare successfully.

The relationship between man and woman itself may be under stress because the second payslip could make the man feel insecure. 'The work is something like a baby coming into the household. The man finds himself competing for attention,' says clinical psychologist Judith Kuriansky, who deals with marriage counselling. A subtle battle for control of the relationship may rage beneath the surface of the marriage. It could undermine both the marriage and the careers.

To prevent this kind of situation they need to sit down and discuss things frankly. 'What are their fears and fantasies? Is he worried that his wife will have an affair with a colleague? What are his concerns about giving up control? Only by bringing it out into the open can you dissipate such problems,' says Dr Kuriansky. The Family Welfare Association can offer help if you want to seek advice. (See Reference List).

A growing number of women are bringing home more money than their husbands earn. Partners may begin to think of their value in the relationship in terms of how much money they are able to contribute. Such competitiveness can work to subvert a partner's career.

'Obviously if a couple has a good relationship, they want each other to go ahead. But they can be carrying over sibling rivalries,' Dr Kuriansky explains. Sibling rivalry creeps into a marriage in the form of criticising a partner's work. Dr Kuriansky asks her clients to write down statements they make about their spouse's work. She then asks them to determine whether they are positive or negative, critical or supportive. 'Step back and distance yourself to gain a different perspective,' she says. 'You may be surprised to discover that you aren't talking to your spouse but to a sister or brother.'

Sibling rivalry is not the only thing that creeps into a marriage from your own family. There are expectations of how one's spouse should act. On the one hand, a man might be attracted to powerful women and want a wife who is more independent and has more status amd more earning power than his mother. On the other hand, he still wants to be mothered by someone who is relatively docile because that is the way he was raised. 'Half the battle is realising what your real attitudes are and whether or not you may be following your parents' patterns,' says Dr Kuriansky.

EXECUTIVE STRESS

Most business executives know that they have a tightrope to walk, balancing between success and failure, vigour and exhaustion, recognition and blame, and that stress accompanies every step. This enormous stress is part of the popular image of the American executive. Picture a harried man or woman, desk piled high, perspiration on the brow, sipping a tenth cup of coffee and occasionally snapping a pencil in desperation. But do not think that this does not apply to you because you are not in the business sector. A prime reason for many of the growing number of resignations by head teachers is stress at work and this applies to a number of different fields. So the examples below can be applied to many people.

This, of course, doesn't quite apply to all executives. There is no denying, however, that their working lives do cause great stress which can have serious consequences physically and mentally. Ulcers, migraine, heart disease, fatigue, depression, anxiety, anger, low self-esteem – these and other symptoms may be the executive's lot if stress is not managed.

But there is heartening news. Even though stress may be an inescapable part of your job you can, with proper techniques, handle it effectively and even turn it to your advantage.

The Source of Stress

If you can identify the sources of stress you have won half the battle to manage and control it. Dr John Howard studied 300 managers in 12 major companies. His research revealed four main factors that seem to cause stress.

■ A feeling of helplessness. When one is prevented from fulfilling one's proper role, one feels impotent and this gives rise to stress. For example, you may work hard to develop reasonable solutions to some tough problems, but are actually unable to put them into action because of constraints within the organization.

■ Uncertainty. Lack of reliable information – on company policy, budgets, procedure – can make it difficult for you to take sound decisions and this situation produces stress.

■ Urgency. The executive day is characterised by a high turnover of different decisions and tasks. It is estimated that, on average, managers do something different every seven minutes. And each one demands great attention and effort. Their jobs are characterised by brevity, fragmentation and stress.

■ Overwork. The general notion of the workload of the executive is accurate – a great deal of work to be accomplished at an unrelenting pace.

Dr Howard's study showed that these factors appeared in all kinds of on-the-job situations. He places these in categories that may seem depressingly familiar to some executives:

■ Poor management or an inadequate boss. For the 300 executives in the study, having to deal with bad management was the single bigggest stress-producing situation. The executives felt that poor planning, bad direction and chronic indecisiveness was the main cause of tension for them.

■ Lack of authority or blurred organizational structure. The second most significant reason for stress was having to do a job with no authority to it. Almost as bad is having to work within the context of fuzzy organizational boundaries in which job descriptions are vague and bosses plentiful.

■ Uncertainty about promotion and recognition. Great stress can result from worrying about career advancement, and if you never receive any praise or recognition from top management. It is also worrying if you do not know what criteria you are being judged by or what steps you should take to get promoted.

■ Company politics. When work becomes political, it becomes stressful – especially when office politics influence promotions, the use of power, transfers and allocation of supplies and equipment.

■ Personnel problems. Executives must manage people. But when those people do not do their jobs, or are themselves troubled by personal problems, the manager bears the burden of stress.

Stress Inoculations
The obvious answer would be to change those situations that

42

cause stress, but achieving this is not so easy. We all know that very often one cannot avoid stressful situations, let alone change them.

The real solution lies in building up your stress resistance. Some experts now recommend that, by changing your approach to stressful situations – your perception of them – you can actually make yourself resistant to stress and its awful consequences.

This means examining our own attitudes. Most people think that stress is something 'out there', but it may not be so. The best way of explaining this is by looking at two different people's reactions to a roller coaster ride. One may go through with it eyes closed, a stiff back, white knuckles and clenched jaws. The other may be a wide-eyed, thrill-seeker relishing every plunge and waiting to do it again. When in 1983 the giant Bell telephone company in the USA was broken up into smaller companies, it was considered a massive shake-up of any corporate structure. Two researchers, Suzanne Kobasa and Salvatore Maddi, studied the attitudes to stress of the executives involved. They found big differences between those who withstood the organizational change, and those who buckled under.

They found that those who were least troubled by the stressful circumstances had fewer illnesses than those who had problems coping with same circumstances. More significantly, Drs Kobasa and Maddi were able to pinpoint what seemed to inoculate the first group against stress.

The key stress-resistance factor, they say, is 'personality hardiness'. 'Hardiness is not the counterpart of a strong mental constitution,' says Dr Maddi. 'Rather, hardiness is a set of beliefs people have about the world and themselves and the interaction between the two.' These beliefs enable the executive to defuse stress by looking at stressful situations in a unique way. Such a person might think: 'the situation is not completely unmanageable; it's something I can control, at least to a degree. And it is not a trivial or a totally insoluble

43

situation – it's actually interesting and important. I don't think of it as threatening; to me it's more of a challenge.'

Such a stress-defusing response enabled some executives in the Bell system break-up to actually enjoy the stresses that were making other executives' lives a nightmare. Fortunately, say Drs Maddi and Kobasa, this frame of mind is not something you have to be born with, it can be encouraged and developed. They have already taught executives the psychological techniques that create a 'stress-busting' outlook. Here are some of the key techniques:

■ Focusing: This involves discovering what is truly stressful to you about a situation and why. Understanding this is the first step towards gaining some control over it.

For example, John has a report to prepare on improving his department's efficiency. The deadline is looming, he hasn't got very far and the pressure is building up. John thinks he knows the reason for his stress: they never give anyone enough time. But then he tries focusing on the situation. He takes a closer look at his emotions and realizes to his surprise that what he is actually feeling is fear. He traces this fear back to school where he was afraid of failure, and often did not tackle his assignments because he was afraid of doing badly. This insight seems to cut his problem down to size and at least make it capable of manipulation.

■ Situational reconstruction: This method disarms stress by looking back at a difficult situation and putting it in perspective. It is most useful when you run smack into an event that causes you great distress and then continues to obsess you. After a stress-creating event, you could try to imagine specific ways that it could have been made worse or improved. The next step is to visualise what you could have done to make the better outcome a reality. Having used this method you may realize that you do have options, that you can exert some control, that you can use imagination to head off future stresses. As Dr Kobasa explains, 'when you realize how much worse it could have been, you know you didn't mess it as much as you might have.'

■ Compensatory self-improvement: Employ this technique when you run up against the 'executive stone wall' – the stressful situation that cannot be changed.

Step one is to be realistic. If no amount of situational reconstruction creates the feeling that a stressful event can be transformed, say Drs Maddi and Kobasa, 'then that event is a given situation, and is best accepted as such.'

Step two is to realize that you can still have control and success in other areas of your life and then set out to prove that to yourself. Think about yourself and select some aspect that can be improved or changed. Thus, if you are afraid of swimming, or feel you lack poise at public occasions, or are impatient with your children, then instead of banging your head against a stone wall at the office, compensate by working to overcome some failing in yourself.

This technique takes the bite out of stress by giving you an added sense of power, by widening your scope of possible actions, and by undercutting obsession with a hopeless situation.

Other stress experts have investigated what distinguishes executives who cope well with stress from those who cannot. They have come up with some surprising data. Many researchers found that the 'competent copers' use simple anti-stress strategies that other executives ignore. Unlike those ravaged by stress, the coping executives:

■ Postpone thinking about problems until an appropriate time.

■ Detect fatigue in themselves at the right time and respond to it by cutting the working day short or taking time off during the week.

■ Size up stressful situations and decide which aspects are worth worrying about and which can be ignored.

■ Delegate tasks to others especially when the pressure begins to build up.

■ Recognise when perfection in completing a task is possible and when it is not.

■ Take regular exercise.

■ Go on holiday.

■ Are not afraid to laugh at themselves.

■ Talk to others – colleagues, friends, spouses – about job pressures.

■ Expect the unexpected. They therefore try to be prepared to find the time and energy to deal with the inevitable stressful events that can appear from nowhere.

Stress First Aid for the Executive

It's just 9.22 in the morning and already your boss is in a lather. Your big project has been knocked on the head and you have already accumulated enough stress to last you all day. Of course, you'll get the mess sorted out eventually, but what can you do for on-the-spot stress relief?

Don't despair say the experts. Here are some of their most effective suggestions for rapid easing of tension so that you can get on with the job of being the top-notch executive.

■ Stretch yourself. Dissipate the tautness in your muscles by giving them a nice long stretch. Select a muscle group (legs, arms, neck, back) and gently and slowly stretch them until you feel a tug, hold for 10 to 30 seconds, then release. You can do this throughout the whole body, or just in the muscles that are tense.

■ Walk it off. When tension is high, don't just sit up. Get up and take your stress for a stroll. A brisk 10– or 15–minute walk can reduce muscular and nervous tension.

■ Take a trip – in your mind. By visualising a stress-free scene that appeals to you, you can actually unwind the tension. Lock the door to your office, sit back and 'see', as vividly as you can, the sandy shores of your next vacation, or a single magnificent rose. Use as many of your five senses as possible to experience your stress-reducing vision.

■ Take a breather. When you are tense your breathing becomes rapid and shallow. Breathe deeply and slowly deliberately. Take seven seconds to inhale and eight to exhale. Carry on the deep breathing for five minutes, or longer if necessary.

■ Practice P.R. The technique known as Progressive Relaxation is a perfect stress-releaser for the office. You may need some privacy (in your office or the cloakroom) the first time you try it. But as you get better you can employ it anywhere.

First, sit down, lean back and close your eyes. Then clench your right hand, tensing the muscles in your wrist and forearm. Hold for five seconds, concentrating on the tension building in your hand. Then release, letting the tension drain away and paying close attention to the feeling of relaxation. Repeat this procedure in your left hand, then your upper arms, shoulders, neck, back, face, legs, feet and toes.

■ Open the pressure valve. If you are steamed up or stressed about something, open your mouth and let out the pressure. This is not foolish advice. Sometimes the quickest way to ease tension is to discuss it calmly with the people who create it for

47

you. If you can talk out the conflicts you're having with someone in a detached manner (without adding fuel to the fire) you'll be able to de-pressurise yourself and the whole situation. Even talking things over with friends outside the situation can help.

Another way to open the stress-release valve is to have a good laugh, or a good cry. Laughing at your predicament can restore calm and give you a more productive perspective. Crying — which every good executive wants to do occasionally, but won't — may help in stress-easing by carrying away some of the body's potentially harmful chemicals in tears.

On-the-Job Stress

Robert Collier Page was once the medical director of the American oil giant Standard Oil Company, now Exxon. In 1963 he wrote a pioneering book on occupational health. He had at one time studied 100 employees who had jobs that did not match their level of intelligence, aptitudes, personality or aspirations. They suffered from sleeplessness, headaches, despondency and stomach problems, amongst other symptoms. On examination they were found not to have any disease; their symptoms seemed to stem from their jobs.

Dr Page wrote, 'If no one else happens to observe what is happening, the individual will continue to push himself blithely into the performance of tasks against which his whole inner being rebels. Eventually this inner being or sub-conscious will strike back in the only way it knows...producing a symptom of illness to warn... that it is time to stop, look and listen.' He goes on to say, 'The same habits of self-deception he has acquired in order to stick to his job will enable him to shrug off the first minor symptoms of potential functional illness...If by this time he is fairly well advanced into his middle years, this creeping loss of health will be progressive and, when he is finally forced to recognise his true predicament, irreversible.' In the decades since that was written, stress has been identified as a major health problem for the working adult population.

In the USA this shows that:

■ Working excessive hours and doing more than one job has been associated with coronary heart disease.

■ Monotonous work creates job dissatisfaction, poor mental health, and leads to coronary heart disease, peptic ulcers and gastritis.

■ Stress created by conflicting job demands has resulted in depression, and physical effects such as increased heart beat rate and blood pressure.

One of the most significant reasons for stress at work is the fact that very often we feel we have no control over our situation. Lack of participation in the decision-making process is linked to low self-esteem.

Secondly, feeling angry at the nature of one's job, and suppressing it, can be harmful. Those who are dissatisfied with their jobs, are angry about it and stifle their resentment, heightening their chances of suffering from high blood pressure.

There are two avenues for action. One is to change the job, which is not always easy. The other is to change your reactions to the job.

Manoeuvring Change

You may be fortunate in getting the support of your boss or colleagues to make changes. Think about these rationally, and devise a sensible plan. Ask your boss for more guidance, freedom, budget allocations, whatever. Or ask your colleagues or trades union to help; it could be the working hours need to be re-examined, or more recreational facilities offered. Some changes can be made through colleague support and negotiation.

If you cannot improve the way you work, you can improve the way you view it. Think of yourself as a waiter in a very busy restaurant. You have an irate customer who wants his meal in a hurry. The best course is to say to him, 'I'm really sorry, but there is an awful rush today and the kitchen is finding it difficult to cope. I haven't forgotten you and I'll go and remind the chef again now.' But, in the end, if you can't stand the heat in the kitchen, you'd better get out.

An unrewarding job also creates stress. You may, however, not be in a position to get out. How can you distance yourself from such stress? Think about the cause of your tension. If you feel that you are not at fault, discuss the situation with someone you trust, not necessarily a psychiatrist, but perhaps someone at work. They might be able to give you an objective opinion. If you then come to the conclusion that your reactions are valid you need to take practical steps:

■ Build up interests outside the job like doing voluntary work that brings you personal satisfaction.

■ Take a course in a hobby, or a professional area that might help you get another job.

■ Talk to people who work in similar jobs, for an insight into their situations.

■ Identify the next stage in your career. Spend a fixed amount of time each day, helping you get there. Thus if you want to go into computers see if there is someone in your own organization who can advise you. If there is a professional organization for your kind of work, or a trades union, contact them. Scan the job re-training schemes, or opportunities offered by local jobs centres.

■ Get out of the building, if only for ten minutes at lunchtime. A walk will relieve stress.

Sometimes you might find yourself in a job in which there is, in fact, not enough stress. If you are the kind of person who works best in pressured environments, and under constant supervision, then working on a long-term project in which all responsibility has been delegated to you, may not be your cup of tea.

Some management techniques now hold that people will perform better if they work at their own pace. This may not suit you. If so, try structuring your own workload to personal deadlines. Tell your boss that you don't feel comfortable about the lack of supervision and arrange to meet every two weeks for a brief progress meeting.

Talking to Colleagues

Ed Donovan of the Boston police force in the USA has learnt that it is crucial to talk to fellow workers.

He had been a police officer for only five years when he felt he could no longer take the strain of the job. It demanded that he be a Superman taking split-second decisions, that he deal with danger calmly and be expected to solve other people's problems, while not having any of his own. The inner-city policeman is subject to more stress than most and Donovan tried to cope by drinking heavily, taking drugs and eventually by trying to shoot himself.

But he couldn't pull the trigger.

Donovan did not trust police psychologists. He felt the only people he could turn to were his peers, his fellow officers, two of whom ran a course to deal with alcoholism in the force. Their support helped him to learn to deal with the stress of his job. Ed Donovan used this experience to launch the Boston Police Department Stress Program and to write a book *The Shattered Badge*.

The programme has been running for 13 years and has helped thousands of policemen, a profession, says Donovan least likely to seek help from mental health experts given, as policeman are, to laying down the law and appearing tough.

The programme relies mainly on peer counselling; professionals are used only as a back-up.

This success underscores three crucial points:

■ There is nothing wrong in admitting that you have difficulty coping with the stress of your job, even if it is less demanding than that of a policeman.

■ There is a great deal of relief to be gained from talking about 'workplace woes' with colleagues you can trust.

■ There may be professional counsellors available at work or through your union if you feel your fellow workers cannot help you to the degree you need or if the exercise becomes one in indulgence. In that case make a start by talking to your doctor, but also look at other organizations who work in the field of mental health who may be able to give you guidance. (See Reference List, Work, Mental Health)

Raising Hopes

There must be occasions when you feel you are worth much more than the salary you receive, and you have been considering asking for a raise. There are probably fewer occasions when your boss has come in and said, 'You've done a great job, we couldn't have done without you'.

Unfortunately bosses can be hostile rather than thoughtful and appreciative. So if you want to improve your working relationship, or ask for a raise, *you* will have to work at it, and then there may be a better chance of getting what you want.

One of the reasons why appeals for a raise fall flat is because you may not have assessed the situation from the boss's point of view. No doubt you have a good estimate of your own worth, but does the boss perceive you as indispensable? Can you make an objective analysis of your achievements in the last few months? Was the increase in production due to increased support staff or your own performance? Make a good case out on paper and then rehearse a presentation of it, making it as persuasive as possible.

You need also to consider that, even though you may be a prime candidate for a raise, there may be constraints on your employers. There are good times and bad times to ask for advancement. So pick your moment. And sometimes the boss will not be able to give you an answer because he may have to consult his superiors and the personnel department. It helps if you have an understanding of the chain of command, and the degree to which your immediate boss will promote your case.

If your request is turned down, make sure you understand why this decision has been made. If it is because of your performance, ask what you can do to improve it. Tell your boss you would appreciate getting feedback on your work and make it clear that you are serious about doing better.

If you have a reasonable case, you still have to learn diplomacy. Look at the reasons you advance and eliminate those that may be considered shaky; focus on the strong points and keep your arguments brief and pithy. That way you increase your chances of getting a reasonable hearing from your boss.

The Wrong Kind of Job

Some people are faced by a promotion that actually makes life more difficult for them. If you are overwhelmed and cannot cope with the new responsibilities, determine whether it is just that you don't like the job, or that you actually do not have the skills to do it properly. It is generally the latter reason. Go to your boss or personnel department and ask for training or advice – this is more a sign of maturity and desire to do well than a sign of incompetence. There are others who are trapped in miserable, stressful jobs, from which they'd like to run away, but the fear of being unemployed prevents them from doing so. They may also be afraid of job-hunting or ending up in a worse situation than before. If you have skills that are in demand then do not be afraid to look elsewhere. Have the confidence to spread your wings.

If, like millions of other people, you are holding down a job that someone else could do easily, then you have to devise a strategy to find a comparable job with a better working environment. Read the situations vacant columns, go to an employment agency, look at the local papers for jobs in local government. Be discreet at work about your plans, but continue to search. You may find a position in a smaller organization, or one closer to home that will provide a change.

FAMILY FEUDS

The warm, loving family is an ideal we all aspire to, but this is often very far from the reality of our own relationship with parents and siblings. So what goes wrong?

One major reason is the fact that we all expect certain things from the family. We want it to offer us intimacy, security, predictability. And above all, we seek approval, even when we are well into middle age. 'The 'approval trap' is the major cause of nearly every dispute with your parents,' says psychologist Lionel Felder. 'That's when you each want each other to conform to your expectations and needs. It can block your feelings of love because you either wish your parents were different, resent that they're not, feel driven to defy or conform to their values, or feel defensive and unloving when you are with them.'

With brothers and sisters, the cause of a feud is often jealousy. In comparing ourselves with our siblings, we can enhance or diminish each other's sense of personal worth. The target might be your sibling's achievements and success, sexuality and beauty, or social relations with other people.

One can also get locked into roles. When we are children our parents and older brothers and sisters have power over us. But as we grow up we must learn to see our relatives through adult eyes. We should recognise our own power and shortcomings and accept the limitations of our relatives. Otherwise we will remain locked in a childlike relationship with our family and may be heading for disappointment.

If you bear a persistent grudge against a relative it colours all your contact with them, whether it is a phone call or a family reunion. But this kind of grudge may also make you feel guilty. Should that person be ill, or die, you feel guilty. Feuds of this nature are self-perpetuating. When someone causes intense anger, sadness or hurt in you, you may react by screaming at them or addressing them accusingly. That prompts your relative to react in the same way, and you get into a vicious circle of negative reactions.

Letting Go

It is possible to release yourself from the clutches of family feuds. You can get out of the narrow adversarial position, making it possible be free of hurt and anger, and begin to see the better side of people you used to dislike.

Try using these tips:

1. Understand the other side. In most feuds, each of you is firmly convinced that the other person is wrong. 'We often assume that we should convert or reform our relatives to our way of thinking,' says Dr Felder. 'We want to prove that we are right.'

But in many cases, there's no right and wrong person. There are just diffferences in opinion – in religious beliefs, political parties, lifestyles, hairstyles, careers, moral values and personalities. And we each fight to prove that our way is right.

The more we keep fighting, the worse it gets. 'What you resist, persists,' says Dr Felder. 'Let's say your mother doesn't like your new girlfriend, and tells you so. The more you try to resist her point of view and try to convince her that she is wrong, the more she will persist in trying to convince you that she's right.'

So, the next time your relative says something you disagree with, try to understand his feelings, experiences and attitudes instead of attacking him. If necessary, do a little homework on that person's attitude and behaviour.

'Vicki, a client of mine, had married a man who came from a different religious and ethnic background,' says Dr Felder. 'Her parents had reacted so strongly to him that had she eloped and they remained at a distance from her parents for years. So I told Vicki to do some research on their point of view. She talked to aunts, uncles and cousins and read several books on intermarriage and on religious identity. The more she understood about the personal and cultural reasons why her family had been so intolerant, the easier it was for her to work through her own resentment.'

2. Be assertive, not aggressive. Understanding the 'problem relative' does not mean you should bow to his or her wishes. On the contrary, you should stand up for yourself. In fact, if you do not assert your rights, you may perpetuate the conflict.

Let's say you have a mother who plays the martyr. 'The martyr parent maintains control by making you feel inappropriately repsonsible for her suffering,' says Dr Felder.

With a parent like that you may feel that you will never win. You either comply with her wishes and feel resentful, or disobey and feel guilty. Either way you lose.

You probably cannot change your parent's attitude, but you can give up your role in the melodrama. 'Next time your dad says, "If you love me, you'll do as I say," don't scream,' says Dr Felder. 'What you should say instead is, "You've fulfilled your responsibility as a parent by sharing your concern with me, so now you can relax. Even though I don't always do what you like, I still love you."

And the next time your brother or sister makes some snide remark that makes you feel inferior, don't take it to heart. 'Stand up for yourself, by saying, in essence, "That hurt, here's why, and here's what I need so I won't be hurt again," says Dr Felder.

3. Try to stay calm when you're under attack. It's not easy to stay calm when your uncle tells you (again) that you'll never amount to anything. Here's a suggestion for keeping your cool.

'Try a 'guilt de-sensitisation' exercise,' says Dr Felder. 'Think of the five most common shots he can fire at you. It could be "You're getting fat", "Why don't you call me more often?", "When are you getting married?", "Are you still wasting your life in that lousy job?," and so on. Record these phrases on a tape recorder and listen to them again and again. The next time you hear them, think to yourself, "There it is, number three again".'

4. Finally, get rid of your rage. You may still need to let off steam in spite of all attempts to be reasonable. 'When you want to scream, and don't do so, your body suffers,' says Dr Feldman. 'Half your muscles are tensed as if to strike back in anger, while the other half work twice as hard to suppress your reaction. It's like trying to drive with one foot on the accelerator and the other on the brake. I know people with family problems who get all sorts of physical symptoms – headaches, backaches and tension – when they visit their family for the holidays.'

Suppressed anger can hold back your spontaneity and warmth, and prevent you from enjoying the company of your relatives. Most of us know how fraught family Christmases can be, despite the fact that we all set out to have a good time.

'Most family members see each other only at large group events,' says Dr Felder. 'But when many egos are gathered together, it's next to impossible to have a relaxed and satisfying conversation with any relative, especially one with whom you have been having trouble. Too often, a few overbearing people dominate the conversation while the rest sit back and pray that it'll be over soon.'

Rather than venting your frustration on the gathered company, try this method of freeing yourself from anger.

Write a scathing letter to a relative you find difficult to cope with, listing every resentment. But don't send it. Or try yelling at the top of your voice into a pillow, or in the car with the windows rolled up. 'Jump up and down and yell "Get off my back!". But do it in private,' says Dr Felder. 'That can be the quickest and easiest way to transform a 'down' mood into laughter and emotional release.'

A few more strategies to encourage a successful meeting with a relative are:

■ Try to do something both of you enjoy. Take your father to a spectator sport, or go shopping with your sister. Ask your overly critical aunt and uncle out for a morning coffee and stroll in the park.

■ See the good points of people. If there is a distance between you and your cousin, try this exercise. Each of you tell the other three things you like about them. Then, instead of concentrating on the 50 things you hate in each other, try remembering those three good points.

■ Set new limits for length and frequency of visits. If your brother comes to visit for a month and drives you crazy after five days, try a five-day visit the next time. Remember, after three days guests can be like fish – they stink.

■ Make touchy subjects off-limits, if necessary. If you have just been divorced and don't want to be questioned about it, tell your relatives you don't want to discuss it. Do tell them you need lots of support and you need the subject to be off-limits because you are sensitive about it.

And keep working at the relationship, because it's worth the effort. People come and go in our lives, but our families are with us forever. (See Reference List, Family Welfare Association).

HOLIDAYS

You've been preparing for this for weeks. It's August Bank Holiday and you have a houseful of friends looking forward to a lovely summer meal. The sun is shining, the wine is plentiful and you have checked the oven every fifteen minutes, but the joint is not yet done. Then realisation dawns, the oven has given up on you. The joint will never be done.

Is your day ruined? Are you going to fume and moan and aplogise, or are you going to rustle up whatever's in the 'fridge and carry on with all the other nice things you have made. In such a situation being inflexible will be of little help. No doubt you are house-proud and hospitable but there is no point in making yourself unhappy and inflicting that on your guests. Flow with the constraints that have been imposed, you can still enjoy the company of your friends.

The holiday season imposes its own form of stress. Christmas is the prime example. Most of us enjoy buying or making presents, going to parties and receiving cards and gifts. But too much of this, and the sometimes hollow ring of forced jollity, can generate stress. It can also heighten certain feelings – if one has been lonely, for example, one feels it more sharply when everyone appears to be out with friends. If you have been separated from a loved one you miss them even more at this time.

Christmas and New Year are a kind of milestone for many people. They mark a change and bring into focus all the issues that have been bothering us through the year. We assess ourselves and the year that has gone by. The popular connotations of the season make us measure ourselves against idealized images of family life. And we can end up feeling unhappy and dissatisfied because we have not passed the test.

It is possible to plan to avoid some of the stress. This is *not* the time to air long-term grievances or regrets, but it is important to make a note of the issues that do arise, particularly within the family, so that you can deal with them, hopefully, *before* next Christmas!

Tradition, Time and Money

Remember the lemon tarts that your mother used to make when she knew the school holidays were coming round, so that you could have a nibble while you were out playing? You may want to do the same for your children, but it's not that easy to knead the dough at night when you are out earning it all day. Women in particular can feel guilty when they realize they can't do everything they think they 'should' to prepare for the holidays.

'Women need to realize they can't be the perfect wife, mother and worker all at the same time,' says psychiatrist Herbert Freudenberger. 'People need to pre-think the holidays,' he says. Try to anticpate what problems may arise and make plans to avoid them.

Rather than trying to do everything themselves, for instance, or abandoning tradition altogether, women need to delegate holiday tasks to their husbands, children, friends and relatives. If you plan to have a party inviting families with children who are also on holiday, ask your guests to bring a dish. Most people would be happy to contribute in this way, and there is less pressure on the hostess.

Or if you are visiting friends, your mother or your sister, be kind to your hostess. Offer to take the whole family out to a meal one day so that she is not tied to the kitchen throughout. To avoid holiday hassles here are some other tips:

■ Do a 'time budget' allowing extra time for driving to the station or airport, getting stuck in traffic, or for simply wrapping gifts. Also keep some daily 'down time' for exercise, a bath, or just a rest.

■ Make a schedule for the things you really want to do, whether it is in the half term or your annual holiday. You could write them in on a big calendar. One tip is to break up a task into various stages; for the lemaon tarts, make the pastry one day the filling another.

■ Take some of the stress out of gift-giving (as Christmas

60

approaches) by shopping at off-peak times. The charity catalogues are another way of choosing presents, ordering by post rather than trudging through the shops. In some cases, for teenagers for example, money may be more welcome than a hastily-bought gift.

Holidays and celebrations like Christmas can be expensive. 'Money is something people absolutely need to look at ahead of time and set limits on,' says Dr Freudenberger. One can still be paying for Christmas in July.

Spending beyond a realistic limit is often a symptom of other problems. A father who is wildly extravagant towards his children at Christmas could be trying to compensate for the time he has not spent with them over the year. 'For others,' says Dr Freudenberger, 'it may be a way of denying the reality of their own financial situation,' especially if they are in debt, or have lost their jobs.

If you are financially strapped, first admit it to yourself. Then talk to the children about what presents the family can afford. 'Unless they're totally spoiled, you'll be surprised how accepting they'll be,' Dr Freudenberger says. 'Say "Daddy's been sick (or laid off, or whatever) and we don't have the money to give the same kind of gifts this year, so let's talk about what we *can* buy".'

Being broke can be a good reason to start moving away from the notion that material things are the only way to express affection. Instead, give the children some things that cost nothing but that they will like: breakfast in bed, teaching them to paint or play cards. And suggest they do the same for others in the family. You can show that you care, *without* presents.

Expectations and Reality
People dream of a white Christmas even if they are in Hawaii or Australia but this, of course, is just a popular notion. The image is hard to dispel, just like childhood hopes about Christmas. We have been primed to be full of expectations and so we are set up to be disappointed.

61

The antidote to this is to take a clear-eyed look at family relationships. Christmas by itself is not going to make them any better. If you want to improve your relationship with a relative, make long-range plans. Try to meet during the year. Write a few letters or talk to them on the phone more frequently. Send them a postcard when you are on holiday. There are many ways of keeping in touch.

If you need to patch things up with someone, don't wait until they walk through the door on Christmas Day. Talk to them a month before, Dr Freudenberger says. 'Clear the air a little bit. Apologise for whatever it is, not calling or writing, and let them express their anger. Let them know you're happy about talking it out, and that you'll be glad to see them in a few weeks.'

Is this the first Christmas since you were divorced? If so, it's very important to plan ahead for your children. Who do they go to and when? And will the children have a say in where they spend their time? If this is going to be the first Christmas for you without your children, it would be wise to go on a winter holiday. You will be with strangers, without any immediate pressures and this might ease the strain of missing the kids.

If, on the other hand, you are introducing the children to a new mother or father or partner, be sensitive to their needs and do some preparation beforehand. This is essential if they are to feel comfortable in the new family, says Dr Freudenberger. 'Have photographs, with the names on them, of the people the children are going to meet. Sit down and talk about the people with your children.' It is also important that the children have some routine during their visit, so that they do not feel lost and at sea in the new situation. Give them some time to themselves to rest and talk, or just play by themselves.

Is this the first holiday since a parent or a grandparent died? Don't wait till the time is upon you, to come to terms with your loss. 'Some of the young people I see feel that they don't have family any more,' Dr Freudenberger says. 'But sometimes they can put together a real family Christmas. They'll invite everyone to their place (or take it in turns). They're amazed to see how many people are just looking for someone to take charge. That tradition, that ritual, can continue if someone in the next generation can pick it up.'

Christmas is a spiritual time of year, whether we are Christian, Jewish or Moslem. It is a good time to look at who we are and how we're living our lives. Try to get away from what you think Christmas *ought* to be and make it what you want it to be. The answer lies in discovering what really gives you pleasure at this time of the year, and how you can best enjoy the company of family and friends.

TRAVEL PLANNING

Going away, whether on holiday or on a lengthy business tour, is always fraught with unexpected problems. Instead of getting off to shaky start make a checklist of all the jobs that have to be done and allocate time for each one. At the office, delegate work so that other people can be in charge and make back-up emergency plans.

At home, there are preparatory tasks:

■ Paying outstanding bills or arranging for expected ones to be dealt with.

■ Arranging for health cover. The E111 form covers most emergency health needs in EEC countries – it can be obtained from the local Department of Social Security office. For countries outside Europe you need independent cover.

■ Arranging for foreign currency or travellers cheques if necessary. Check if you need a visa if you are going to a non-EEC country, or an Eastern bloc country.

■ Checking the car if you are driving, and taking out relevant insurance as well. If you are a member of a motoring organization they can help with maps and routes as well as an international driving licence (extra payment for non-members).

■ Making arrangements for the mail, the milk, the newspapers, the family pet, the pot plants.

■ Leaving a detailed itinerary with someone you trust, with contact addreses and phone numbers.

The night before you leave:

■ Make sure you have packed all you need. Use two cases; if one gets lost you will still have some clothes. Remove old baggage tags – they can confuse loading.

■ Check you have put in the presents, if visiting family or friends.

■ Do you need any medicines to take with you?

On the day itself allow ample time for:

■ Checking appliances and doors and windows.

■ Leaving keys with neighbours or friends

■ Driving to airport or station.

■ Putting passports and tickets in safe, retrievable place.

Doing Your Homework

'I was once in Siberia,' says author Paul Theroux (also well known for setting his books in faraway places) 'and I recall an Australian saying to me in a complaining way, 'It's cold here!'. In Peru, an American woman said to me, 'I hate these hills – they're too steep'. We were in the Andes.'

Not all travellers would be so foolish as to choose a holiday they would be uncomfortable with, but many often make themselves so because they have not planned their holiday well. Whether you are going to Southend or San Tropez, do your homework.

■ If you feel you'd like to go an an activity holiday – skiing, hiking, art tours – research the opportunities thoroughly. Go to several travel agents to see what they offer and choose a reliable one, affiliated to the Association of British Travel Agents.

■ Make a list of your specifications – self-catering, rooms with bath, by the sea etc – and make sure the agent knows what they are.

■ Make reservations well in advance, and confirm them through early payment. If you are flying, check times of departure and baggage rules. Some charter flights have special restrictions on weight.

■ Learn more about your destination, if you have not been there before. If it is a destination where English is not widely spoken, be sure to have a good guide book and a couple of novels to read.

If, after all your planning, the sun refuses to shine on a beach holiday, or the snows melt before you can go skiing, be ready for alternative action. Improvise for the remainder of your trip, rather than feeling sorry for yourself. Explore the surrounding areas – there are generally picturesque or historic places to be visited. Find the local market or fair. Catch up on letter-writing. Time is never wasted if you have a genuine interest in enjoying yourself.

LONELINESS

A feeling of isolation, of being cut off from others, of a loss of self-esteem; loneliness is each and all of these. It afflicts not just the elderly, but many young people as well. In fact this black emotion is felt most acutely in late adolescence as we grow into young adults.

The music that young people at this age enjoy is reflective of their feelings. But that loneliness tapers off as they pair into permanent or semi-permanent relationships. At the same time they gain more self-confidence, an acquisition that makes the world less threatening and thus makes them less vulnerable to loneliness.

The isolation of the older person, perhaps widowed and living on their own, is of a different nature. They have been through the process of growing up and making contact with people, establishing families and seeing these fall away. Their's is a situation imposed, perhaps, by society and inadequate social support. But for the young, the situation is very different.

As they grow up, young people may not have much confidence and may blame themselves for their loneliness. They feel that they lack social skills and are not good-looking enough to attract company. Or they might be removed from their own usual surroundings – changing schools, being separated from parents or the customary school gang. This is akin to the loneliness that anyone can feel at being separated from their natural situation — moving house, getting divorced, or losing a partner. Change from an established and familiar place to one of uncertainty can be very disturbing.

So if you feel lonely try to find out the cause. Then it is only natural that you should try to remedy the situation. But do not feel helpless or blame yourself!

Making Changes

If you've diagnosed your loneliness as a passing phase you can make it move on faster. Start to focus your energy on activities that will put you in touch with both yourself and others.

■ First: Push the loneliness to the back of your mind and devote some time, no matter how little, to an activity – hobby, sport or spiritual pursuit – that you can do on your own. Do something that you enjoy doing on your own and does not depend on other people. This will help you build self-reliance, a trait that others will appreciate.

■ Next: Find an activity which involves other people: voluntary work or an evening class where you will meet like-minded people. This could be helping at a creche, or a carpentry class. If you like sport, find a local sports centre, or tennis club. Try to pick something that you feel comfortable with, and not over competitive.

If you have recently lost a spouse and are finding it hard to adjust to your widowed state, take it in stages.

■ You can climb out of your depression by first reaching into it. There is no real solution to your loss; you can come to terms with it by first wallowing in it. Have a good cry. Feel sorry for yourself. Don't try to share this with anyone. When you are ready for other people, you'll emerge like a butterfly from a cocoon.

■ Release yourself from anger. Try this strategy: There is a lot of frustration and anger simmering in you, so when you're in one of these moods, pick out someone you really dislike intensely, or are jealous of. Do something for him or her. Make them a present, or invite them out for a meal. Even though you may be free of just a fraction of your anger, this act of generosity will make you begin to feel better.

If, on the other hand, your loneliness is linked to growing older or retirement, plan ahead for this stage of your life.

■ Develop a network of friends who share the same situation.

■ Try to be active. Getting out of the house, while giving you some exercise, increases contact with other people and makes one feel one is still in touch with life. If you have a problem with mobility, see if the local Social Services office has any solutions. Investigate recreational facilities for older people.

■ If you do not have grandchildren, or do not see them often, try to maintain contact with young people. Perhaps you could have a neighbour's child over to bake a cake together. Children bring energy and vitality that will pep you up as well.

It has been shown that long-term isolation and lack of human companionship, which are conditions of the mind, have serious effects on our physical wellbeing. The sudden loss of a loved one is a common cause of loneliness and often leads to the early death of the remaining partner. Chronic loneliness has a profound effect on us; it makes us more vulnerable to serious illness. In the USA, say researchers, this is particularly apparent in heart disease, the leading cause of death in the country. Millions of people are dying, quite literally, of broken or lonely hearts.

Getting to Know You

The only way to end chronic loneliness is to make friends; this needs self-confidence and social skills that many people do not have. They can, however, be learnt. In fact the curriculum in many schools today has a component that teaches young people how to manage their lives and deal fruitfully with society. These courses increase their confidence and endow them with the ability to 'interact' successfully with other people.

But there are many of us who have not had the advantage of such teaching and are, perhaps, painfully shy and fearful of venturing an opinion or striking up a conversation with strangers. What you need is a friend and you can take some strategic steps to overcome your lack of confidence.

■ If you are at a party, do not position yourself in a corner. Scan the guests and select a small group of people, not a twosome, who appear less intimidating to you.

■ Try entering the conversation at an appropriate point, with an appreciative comment about your host or hostess, the food or the decor.

■ Remind yourself to ask questions and listen to the responses of others.

■ If you meet someone with the same interests, do not assume that you are of no interest to them. Take a name or a phone number and say you would like to meet for a coffee. If the other person reponds warmly, go ahead. If they do not, do not be disheartened. If you have confidence in yourself, other people will warm to you.

Making a friend is very much a matter of creating a warm relationship with them, one based on trust. Many people, and most often men, find it difficult to do this. Men socialise as much as women, but women are able to establish an intimate friendship. Men find it difficult to talk about their feelings, and it is this exchange of thought and emotion that creates a sense of security and keeps away feelings of loneliness.

■ Start by making a list of possible people you could talk to who could develop into rewarding friends.

■ Find an occasion at which you have the time to talk to someone in depth. Express your thoughts and feelings openly, perhaps about some anxiety or fear, things that others don't usually talk about. You may find the other person responds in like manner.

■ Don't keep searching for the ideal romantic relationship. A firm friendship is often a better antidote to loneliness than the search for the ideal lover. In the process you might lose opportunities for making good friends.

STAGE FRIGHT

Have you ever had to face an audience and been overcome by nerves? The symptoms are all too familiar: sweaty palms, shaking voice, rubbery legs. This is stage fright, a 'fight-or-flight' reaction, and it is caused by our fear of doing anything in public that could result in social humiliation. Women drivers fear reversing while the men watch. Company executives approach the presentation of their departmental budget with trepidation, and interviewees shiver before the examining board.

The 'fight-or-flight' syndrome is caused by physical changes within us. The adrenal glands shoot the hormone adrenaline into the bloodstream. This prepares the body for an unusual performance. The heartbeat rate increases, as does blood pressure. In a sense, one is primed for action. Sportsmen know that they need this boost just before their race. But for others it is pure anxiety and a terrible symptom of fear.

Relaxation and Positive Thinking

You can overcome your fear. If you are only called upon to perform occasionally, then ready yourself by rehearsing thoroughly. Avoid alcohol or stimulants like coffee before you are due to go on. Tranquillisers are little use as well as they may slow you down too much.

Relaxation is the key, especially if you are called to work in public fairly regularly. Here are a few techniques:

■ Systematic desensitisation. Relax your muscles. Imagine speaking to a few people and then progressively to larger audiences, till you are finally in a huge auditorium.

■ Flooding. Confront your fear directly. This means trying

70

your speech out, without prevarication, on a group. This could be the staff room at school or members of your office department.

■ Modelling. Watch some successful public figure on television very closely. By observing them, and their method of addressing people, you can lose some of your fear of the public.

If you are still terrified of appearing on such occasions, or turn down a promotion because the job requires some public speaking, you could go to your doctor. He may prescribe a 'beta-blocker', the medicine propanolol, which blocks the effects of the adrenaline. But this is only to be advised in the most extreme cases.

Positive thinking, first advocated by Dale Carnegie, author of the trendsetting *How to Win Friends and Influence People* decades ago, is a great ally. Carnegie's philosophy is that anyone can speak in public if they have self-confidence and a strong desire to communicate their ideas. To develop that confidence one has to do whatever one fears doing and tuck a record of successful experiences under one's belt.

WORKAHOLISM

Popular notions of the workaholic as a person driving himself to ill-health are not really accurate say experts today. People whose life is their work find fulfillment in it, rather than in fishing or tennis or the opera. They are doing what they like. You will not usually find workaholics in jobs that don't interest them!

It is the *inflexible* addiction to work that is cause for concern. If you look upon work as the answer to some problem, or use it to avoid other situations, or if the need for power or manipulation becomes the overriding motive for the commitment to your job, then your health may be at risk.

Leave a workaholic at his job for 24 hours a day, seven days a week and he may be quite happy and satisfied. It is when he has to interact with non-workaholics that problems arise. Not everyone can, or wants to, work at this furious pace. Colleagues who aren't so inclined will feel uncomfortable or resentful if they are expected to do the same. It is also easy to be angry with a spouse who is actually married to work and treats him or her with somewhat less regard.

Fears that workaholics shorten their lives through stress may be unfounded. It actually depends on the individual's response to stress. Some people thrive on it. If they are deeply involved with their jobs, they feel they can exert some control over it and anticipate change as an exciting challenge. Others may be incapacitated by the same level of stress, regardless of the potential rewards for the pysche.

So find out what kind of workaholic you are. It is an enormously egotistical thing to be one, but if you genuinely delight in work and relate well to other people and your family, you are an integrated person. On the other hand, if you search within yourself and find that this addiction is really an escape, or that your self-esteem is linked to how much money you make, think again.

Our cultural background has sometimes conditioned us to working very hard. In school or college this may be a question of being ultra-comptetive, and the corporate culture can enhance this. But unless you work for an understaffed organization there should be no compulsion to work a 60–hour week. In fact some management analysts could say this is a sign of inefficiency! The truth may be that you are wasting some 10 hours a week on trivialities or 'make-work' projects. Use those hours for 'play' rather than work, but it can be play of a different nature — voluntary work for example, or pursuing a hobby.

Family Time
Your family needs you and if you have taken the decision to reduce your working week, give the time saved to them.

■ Schedule some regular time for your spouse. Make it a

specific evening of the week and get a babysitter. If there happens to be a series of films or plays or spectator sport, buy a set of tickets in advance. That way you will commit the time to being together.

■ Share some new activity with your spouse – strawberry-picking or walking trips. But don't be obssesive so that it becomes just like work.

■ Share a new activity with your family. Sorting out the stamp collection once a week, playing football or badminton, or fishing.

■ If because of work you have missed your child's performance in the school play, ask what else they would like to do with you instead. It may be going out cycling together. On a weekend try to write in some time on your calendar for playing with your children.

■ Write in some 'intimacy' time for your spouse too. Being together, and alone, is very important, whether it is for making love or just pure companionship.

■ Keep things in perspective. Do you want your family to be last on the list? You are really more valuable to those at home, than those at work. Your parents will appreciate your being present at their golden anniversary celebration much more than colleagues at a company dinner. If you talk to your family they wil tell you if their needs are not being met.

You may be the partner of a workaholic who is unable to change and find more time for you. If you feel resentful, you may be quite justified. You married because you wanted to share things. But this is not how they have worked out.

You could try asking them to change, to find less pleasure in work and more in your company. He or she may respond with genuine promises of change, but sometimes they will remain only promises. Getting ahead at work can mean not stopping on the corporate ladder, but moving upwards. Let us assume that you will stay with your workaholic spouse whether or not they decide to spend more time with you. Keep in mind that your life together will abound in compromises made by you. After that try to capitalise on the situation.

■ Try to interest your spouse in activities that you both enjoyed before work became such a preoccupation – if such activities existed.

■ Alternatively, see if a new activity can be shared in scheduled 'play' time. If this does not work, develop interests of your own. Don't let your spouse's non-cooperation rob you of enjoyment.

■ Make the time you spend together as enjoyable as possible. If housework gets in the way, and you can afford some help, invest in it, rather than let the time be wasted on chores.

Should your spouse decide that he or she will try to change expect some trouble even then. Readjustments will have to be made. You and the family have got used to playing second fiddle, so putting what you want first may be difficult. Your spouse may be irritable at having to give up rewarding work for possibly unrewarding family life. Expect them to be depressed, but approach the situation gently and don't overdo the attention.

The Workaholic Boss

If you are taking up a new job you may be able to find out the way your prospective boss regards work. Ask questions about the hours generally put in, or about the past career of your new boss. This may reveal that he was a glutton for hard work, packing in part-time jobs as a student, or extra courses and responsibilities in the office.

74

If in the end you find yourself with a boss who works long hours and expects it of others then rather than challenge the working pattern, you should accept it and see how best you can adapt it for yourself. The first point to remember is that you will probably be able to sustain the role if you know it is for a specific period. Some people accept a job with a workaholic boss only long enough to gain experience to move on. This strategy is wise only if you know that something better lies ahead of you. Another strategy is to try to discuss it with your boss saying that the style of operation isn't one that you can comfortably follow and that your productivity is tuned to a different method. This has a reasonable chance of success, but you must first show that you have top-notch work if you are to command any respect for your point of view.

In the ultimate analysis a square peg will not fit a round hole, so try to find a niche that suits you.

On the other hand you may find you have a boss who gets by with the minimum and that you are the workaholic. You could have surmised that the powers-that-be would be pleased to have you in their team. In reality the opposite may be true. Many bosses, particularly in large, competitive organizations feel threatened by a dedicated subordinate. They could feel that you are after their job.

In such a situation tell your boss that you merely enjoy working endless overtime and have no ambitions to replace him or her. They may not necessarily believe you, but may suggest you find extramural ways of spending your energy. If you are a graphic designer you could join a professional association and work on their newsletter, or you could organize the staff association recreational activities.

If you are a committed worker, be politic in your relationship with your boss and colleagues. Try not to make the former insecure, or the latter jealous. This approach will not add to the possible stress of being a workaholic!

2

CONTROLLING SELF-MADE STRESS

Anger ■ *Guilt* ■ *Perfectionism*

Phobias and Panic Attacks

Risk-Taking ■ *Type A Behaviour*

Worrying

ANGER

In Japan a person who feels angry is not likely to subject the cause of his anger to a torrent of furious words. He will, instead, show it by excessive politeness and a neutral expression.

The Utku Inuit generally ostracise those who lose their temper, regradless of the reason for the outburst.

Virtually every culture has its own way of coping with anger, and permissible methods of expressing it. In the west it has been popularly held that one should get rid of one's anger, rather than suppress it because the latter results in tension, nervous breakdowns, ulcers and heart attacks. Now some experts feel that such a universal link between anger and physical ills may be overstated and that people who express their anger without hesitation or reflection may want to consider the consequences. Sometimes the 'let it all hang out' philosophy is counterproductive.

Some research has shown that there is a possible link between the suppression of anger and the development of ulcers. It suggests says Dr Ernest Harburg, senior research scientist at the University of Michigan, that two factors may come into play. The first is the way we have been socialized or brought up. The second is a genetic link: some people are more prone to ulcers regardless of whether they stifle their anger, or not.

Dr Harburg studied 2,300 people in Detroit. Their levels of blood pressure showed that, irrespective of the way they reacted (suppression or expression), significant numbers of people had high levels of blood pressure in response to feeling angry. Yet other studies by the same team showed that unexpressed anger was linked to early death. One is not yet quite sure of the exact nature of the relationship between anger and ill health. Fortunately there are good ways of coping with it, rather than blowing one's top.

Reflective Coping

Bottling up anger and blowing your top are both reflex actions. You don't consider your reaction beforehand, it just happens. You certainly don't think constructively about analysing it, or getting to the root cause. That is why many psychologists recommend reflective coping as a means of dealing with the situation. Don't lash out and don't sit and stew. Instead, think about the source of your anger and the consequences of your response. 'People who respond with reflective handling of anger seem to have lower blood pressure, on average,' says Dr Harburg.

There are two things to keep in mind:

■ Our culture and society teaches us its way of dealing with anger. That is why the Inuit reaction differs from that of the Japanese. Similarly we can learn new ways of tackling this emotion. One way is to keep a diary, so that you can track the ebbs and flows and your responses. Or learn relaxation techniques to encounter the anger and defuse it.

■ Reflective coping does not mean that you cannot tell a boss or a loved one precisely how you feel. The difference this time is that you do it in a constructive manner.

If your boss flings open the door and shouts, 'Where's that report you owe me? Haven't you finished it yet?' and you have, in fact, placed it on his desk, but he hasn't seen it, don't retaliate by shouting back at him. Simply stand up, look him in the eye and say, 'I've already put it on your desk. And I don't like it when you yell at me like that.'

Reason it Out

When you give vent to your anger you are making two statements. You wish to draw the other person's attention to the fact that there is something wrong which should be

79

rectified and secondly, you want to make them feel as unhappy as you do.

Most people seek recourse to anger because it is the only way to highlight the seriousness of the issue, and our society finds this acceptable. But to lose your temper routinely (shouting at the children), feeling better temporarily, and then feeling remorseful about the outburst is not a wise way of solving the underlying problem (untidy bedrooms).

Some experts believe that one should lose one's temper only in circumstances that satisfy three conditions:

■ When it represents a legitimate plea for justice.

■ When it is directed at someone who is the cause of the anger.

■ When getting angry would actually solve the problem and not result in further retaliation.

A rational response to anger is not always possible. Dr Albert Ellis offers step-by-step advice on how to change and undercut irrational reactions.

■ Acknowledge that it's *you* who creates the anger. Someone may displease or frustrate you, but they don't create the anger.

■ Rate people's behaviour instead of evaluating them as a whole. There are people who may do 'bad' things but they are not rotten all the way through.

■ These two steps will help to diminish the anger you feel. The third step is to decide whether to assert yourself or not.

If it's a friend or one of the family, you can tell them how you feel. You can be assertive now, without the fear of

80

alienating the other person, because you have thought about your reaction rationally. The other person, however, may not be one you can properly vent your anger on (the boss) without harmful consequences. In such a case, explain the situation to a friend, as a way of tackling your feelings.

Anger is sometimes the cumulative result of earlier aggravations. If you feel an attack coming on, try taking deep breaths and counting to ten. If you get beyond this point without losing your temper, and if you have the time, you can analyse what makes you angry. Avoid people who cause you do do so. If you can't avoid them, you may be able to anticipate what they are likely to do that annoys you. This will prepare you for alternative ways of coping with this strong and, what some feel, is an uncontrollable, emotion. But perhaps you now know better.

Frustration

How would you cope if you were the young British gymnast who was told at the last minute that you had been selected for the Olympics, but despite everybody's best efforts could not make it in time to Seoul?

That must surely be a frustration of Olympean nature, quite different from the minor tussles with traffic jams or busy telephone numbers. Yet some of us cannot distinguish between the major and minor causes of frustration, reacting to them with equal vehemence when things do not turn out the way we want and feel thwarted as a result.

The way we handle this emotion is influenced by two main factors. In part this is due to our inherited personality, the genetic element – we are not all born with the same temperament. The other is the way we have been reared or grown up – our particular environment has shaped the way we handle upsets.

It is quite human and normal to feel frustrated at being foiled by some situation beyond one's control – if you are cooking a special meal and need quail's eggs and the supermarket does not have them! But you should be able to put this

81

minor event into perspective – the eggs are a delicacy and more likely to be available at a specialist shop. If you still feel intense frustration and anger, then you need to take a good look at your reaction.

So, if dealing with your boss is a cause of constant stress and friction, if you condemn all train ticket sellers as incompetent because you had to wait a few minutes for your change, or if your last parking ticket made you curse all traffic wardens, your frustation might be caused by an inability to deal with authority figures.

Try to look behind the immediate situation and discern a pattern to your reactions. The most common answer to the 'authority figure' reaction is your relationship with your father in childhood, but it could be either parent or another person altogether. Now that you are an adult, you should try not to be resentful of people who, sometimes unfortunately, have certain powers. Most importantly do realize that your boss is not your father.

Whatever the situation that causes frustration, you can take some action.

Behavioural psychologist Dr Allan Markle has these tips:

■ Decide if you can take alternative action – a different route for a traffic jam – and take it.

■ Don't 'awfulize'. Put things in perspective. Missing the last post for an urgent letter is not the same thing as your house burning down. Think how often you say, 'My god, this is dreadful, it's the end of the world!'. If it happens regularly every week, you're 'awfulizing' and you need to temper your thoughts.

■ Don't dwell on past mishaps. If you are constantly reciting to yourself all your past failures, stop! A good technique is to slap your thigh, or snap a rubber band against your wrist every time you catch yourself dwelling on past frustrations.

■ If the problem eludes all the above techniques, think seriously about learning relaxation techniques or practising meditation.

Finally, as the Roman playwright Laberius said 2000 years ago, *Non possunt primi esse omnes in omni tempore:* All of us cannot be first all the time. Accept life's fizzles. Frustration is the price one pays for trying to get things done, perhaps trying to do things better than anyone else. But you do not need to pay too high a price.

GUILT

Like crime, guilt is commonly associated with punishment. It is a powerful emotion whose complexities have been analysed by successive generations of therapists and psychologists. For some time it was popularly thought that guilt was a 'useless' emotion. It was wise to banish guilt and its stressful side effects from the psyche. Now therapists believe that guilt has a place in our psychology. It is a reminder of certain values that we hold and may have betrayed.

The punishment is one we mete out to ourselves, but it can be healthy and constructive if we realize that we have done something wrong, like criticizing a colleague which, on reflection, we decide, was not justified. The natural consequence would be to apologize, or make up the injury in some other way.

Unhealthy or unrealistic feelings of guilt result from other situations. Let's say your mother dies. You search the past for occasions when you might have neglected her, or let her down. This becomes a preoccupation with you and then you begin to feel that you don't deserve to do well as a result. You are punishing yourself.

Guilt is the agonizing feeling that you have done something wrong, or betrayed your own values. This causes us anxiety and stress, so we have to decide whether these feelings are capable of being productive or destructive.

83

Culture, society and family nurture our values and those to which we ascribe a sense of guilt. In childhood we are taught that certain things are not done, feasible or appropriate. Some of those concepts however are no longer applicable today. For example, despite women's liberation many women, especially those with families, still feel ambivalent about their work. Again many women, brought up on taboos about sex, or discussion of it, are trapped between healthy sexual appetite and childhood values.

Manipulation

Guilt can be a tool for manipulating people, so follow your feelings through and see where you emotions came from. Very often, says Dr Harry Gunn, people can trace their feelings to their parents. Occasionally, this can have a powerful hold on one and it may take professional psychotherapy to flush it out of your system. (See Reference List, Family Welfare Association).

Dr Gunn recalls a former client who was a talented swimmer and joined the US Navy to become a frogman. He, however, felt acute anxiety when he embarked on solo dives. In the course of his therapy with Dr Gunn it emerged that at the age of five or six he loved swimming, but his parents were terrified of the water. His mother, who had a heart condition, told him repeatedly that if he swam alone and needed to be rescued by her, it would result in her death. Twenty years later this influenced his reaction to solo swimming, a reaction that may have been justified at five, but not at 25.

This is unconscious guilt, and it may cause problems that you do not even realize are due to deep, buried fears. To tackle this, try reflecting on what caused the anxiety. See if you can discuss this with a spouse, a partner or a trusted friend.

Breaking Free

A sensible and healthy feeling of guilt – remorse – is a

recognition that you have wilfully acted to hurt another person. On the other hand guilt can lead you to blow things out of proportion or to make a moral judgement – you are a 'bad' person. Both of these are distortions. Another is assuming responsibility for problems you did not actually cause.

One of the reasons for these kinds of distortions is that the person has poor self-esteem, and so seizes upon any situation where they did something wrong. Cognitive therapy can help to get to the root of such situations, strengthen the personality and enhance self-esteem.

Here are some of the signs that you are wallowing in unhealthy guilt:

■ Feeling vaguely guilty, even when there is nothing to feel guilty about.

■ Feeling guilty about being happy, or about something good that has happened.

■ Turning your guilt into anger because it is easier to express anger that to admit guilt.

■ Feeling guilty about an incident that occurred 20 years ago.

Then question yourself about these feelings. Are they intense? Are you paralysed after you have been unkind to your spouse?

Does this behaviour:

■ Get you into more difficulties?

■ Cause you to lose friends?

■ Lead to people rejecting you?

85

■ Make you critical of yourelf and your attitudes?

■ Diminish your enthusiasm for positive action?

After you have considered all these points, take heart. The best thing is to deal with your guilty feelings quickly and efficiently. If you decide that you have, in fact, done something wrong, *own up to it*. Next, take action to rectify your mistake.

And then let go of the guilt. This is the best course, because if you don't, you continue to feel angry and burdened and get into a spiral of guilt. So cleanse yourself of the guilt by doing your best and then letting go.

PERFECTIONISM

It may sound a paradox but perfectionists are bound to be disappointed in their lives. Such people are convinced that total failure lies ahead unless *everything* is done *perfectly*. But they have set themelves unrealistic goals – perfection is unobtainable.

Dr David Burns made a study of over 700 men and women. He discovered that perfectionists were stressed and dissatisfied with their careers and personal lives. He did not find any evidence that showed that they were more successful than their 'non-perfectionist' peers.

Assess your own attitudes by asking whether you:

■ Believe that your worth depends on being best at everything you attempt?

■ Overlook your achievements and concentrate on your failings?

■ Look for the next challenge, rather than enjoying the rewards of the task you have just accomplished?

■ Delay when faced by a project that will be judged by others?

If you answered 'yes' to these questions, then you have all the makings of a perfectionist. You need to sit back and think about ways of tackling this stress-inducing behaviour.

■ Recognize that it is a good thing to set high standards for yourself, but don't judge yourself harshly if you fail to meet them in full. Give yourself permission to be imperfect.

■ Be selective. Concentrate on a few tasks that you really want to excel at instead of squandering your efforts on a number of projects.

■ If you dawdle over a job because you do not really want to be judged, remind yourself that you will do your best and start working. Don't procrastinate out of fear, but get on with the task in hand.

Change Your Thinking

The perfectionist is critical of himself or herself. One needs to identify those patterns of thought that lead to stress or to judgement and thence to depression.

You will soon see a self-defeating process in action:

■ Over-generalising. 'I didn't really get up to scratch. In fact I'm falling down on the job and am no good at it.'

■ Two-way thinking. 'I'm really good at some things and I'm a failure at others.'

■ Selective thinking. 'Once I accomplish something, that achievement becomes insignificant.'

Instead of indulging in such negative thought, turn your desire to the best advantage.

■ Become aware of the gains that *you* get out of being a perfectionist. See yourself as a special person because you demand much of yourself.

■ Direct your concentration – focus it on the task, not on the outcome.

■ Create a 'coping dialogue' with yourself. 'Here I go again, already worrying about the future. Let me just settle down to do my best.' or, 'Dear God, I've only got a day to do this. Hang on, perhaps I should make a list of the most important points first.'

Examine your views on what makes you feel a worthwhile human being. Is it based on:

■ gaining the approval of everyone who is important to you?

■ the ability to perform better that others?

Many people have grown up in perfectionist families where worth has been determined by performance, says psychologist Dr Debra White. In such homes, simply 'being' is not good enough. 'Standards for what is 'good' and 'bad' are set from the outside, not from within, and have clear demarcations: a grade 'A' is acceptable, a high 'B', a failure. There is nothing in between. Spontaneous and creative expression becomes risky and is muffled out of fear of disapproval.'

If your anxiety over achieving perfection is taking a physical and mental toll, remind yourself that nobody is perfect. Think about the underlying causes of the anxiety and you will soon see that perfection alone will not bring you any greater love or feeling of self-esteem. So begin to accept yourself as you are and reduce the stress.

PHOBIAS AND PANIC ATTACKS

Everyone is afraid of something, whether it is riding on a roller coaster, going out on a dark night or facing a snappy dog. These are reasonable fears. A phobia, is irrational. It is a dread of being trapped in a situation that would not trouble most people, like going out in open spaces. Called agoraphobia, it makes people afraid to go to the shops or take a bus, particularly on their own. The opposite to this is claustrophobia, the fear of confined spaces. This makes people shrink from entering lifts, going to the cinema, or travelling in an aeroplane because they are afraid they would not be able to get out.

These are two common phobias, but others include:

■ Social phobias: fear of speaking in public, or of performing some task in sight of others.

■ Simple phobias: fear of cats, snakes, spiders and the like.

■ Blood/injury phobias: fear of the sight of blood, or medical intervention such as receiving an injection.

A person who has intense fears will go to great lengths to rearrange their life so that they do not encounter that fearful situation. Many people suffer from phobias but they have often been dismissed by others as 'just nerves' or have been handed tranquillisers instead of proper treatment. There are self-help associations who can give you more information. (See Reference List)

Don't Panic

'Phobic people are usually bright, energetic, successful, otherwise healthy and above average in many ways,' says Jerilyn Ross, co-founder and President of the Phobia Society of America. 'On the surface they are strong, able to remain calm in a crisis and even to pull others together.' Then one day, while driving to work or standing in the supermarket check-out queue, they suddenly feel sheer panic.

The first time this happens it is like having a heart attack: shortness of breath, palpitations, chest pain or discomfort, choking, dizziness. The person believes he or she is going crazy or losing control. If the episode recurs within the next few weeks (as it often does) the person begins to fear the panic itself. They try to reduce the risk of this happening again by avoiding what they believe triggers these attacks. This is a classic 'fight-or-flight' response with the emphasis on 'flight'.

Many people experience their first sense of acute fear when they are going through some major change in life. This may be a bereavement, getting married or divorced, having a baby, moving away from home, being seriously ill. This stress is measured in 'life change' units; bereavement and divorce top the list of stressful events. There are any number of other situations that create stress – a child leaving home, financial problems, or trouble at work. People may be vulnerable at this time and the fear may hit them in an area in which they had previously no problem, like driving their car. If a young woman has been part of a car pool to take the children to school she may suddenly cry off with headaches, or other appointments, anything to avoid driving.

The 'flight' reaction makes the anticipation of the phobia even worse, so that the panic is in fact twofold. The phobic lives in a constant state of 'what if', fearfully avoiding activities that were previously pursued without anxiety. A phobia is almost as much a cause of stress as a reaction to it.

One can, of course, avoid certain activities – not going into lifts, or flying or driving. But this does make people feel cowardly; they know their fears are irrational and their self-esteem suffers. However, keeping out of the way of the stress does reduce anxiety, but it can be unhealthy – agoraphobics can become housebound; staying away from the doctor will also do you no good if you need attention.

There are two ways of solving the problem. The first is helping yourself. The second is relying on drugs.

Self-Help

Jerilyn Ross overcame a fear of heights. As President of the Phobic Society of America, she says they teach people how to deal with the anxiety itself, so they learn not to fear the fear. 'Using rational arguments to try to convince a phobic that they shouldn't be afraid just doesn't work. Telling someone who is afraid of flying or driving that nothing will happen is like saying to someone about to step into a lion cage, 'Don't worry, he hasn't eaten anyone today'. For a phobic, the fear is very real, it feels like a matter of life and death.'

One of the ways of helping to decrease fear is called exposure therapy. This consists of a gradual, supervised exposure to the frightening object or experience. People who are afraid of flying, for example, take part in a course in which they are introduced to flying, and taken on rides in an aircraft. Because this is done by experts in a controlled setting it gives the person confidence, and increases a sense of familiarity with the very situation that used to cause them stress.

Whether or not you choose to go on one of these courses, you can make use of these tools to help overcome a phobia:

■ Ride out the wave of anxiety. Few people realize that the fear gripping them will only last a minute or two and then subside. They never give themselves the chance to 'sit it out' because they tend to flee instantaneously from the panic attack which, experts say, generally lasts about 20 seconds. So instead of saying to yourself, 'My God, here it goes again,' and then working yourself into a panic, say, 'Even though I'm terrified, this is going to pass.' You'll see that it will.

■ Give youself a means of escape. Most phobias are due to a fear of being trapped. This happens for example at a cinema

91

theatre. To lessen the chances of your feeling a sense of panic, make sure you have an aisle seat. Agree with your companion that if you begin to feel uneasy you would like to go out for a breath of fresh air. If you know that you have means of getting out, the panic may not arise. If you are afraid of the dentist's chair, say to him in advance, 'I am terrified. If I feel I need a respite, I'll hold up my hand, so will you will stop?'

■ Cut down on alcohol and caffeine. If you try to calm yourself with a stiff drink before an anticipated feared experience, you may be doing yourself a disservice. If you drink too much you will begin to feel helpless and create more panic for yourself. Caffeine triggers the release of adrenaline, which is linked to panic attacks. Decaffeinated coffee and non-alcoholic drinks (beer) or a low-alcohol glass of wine are much more sensible.

Seeking Help

If you find that your phobia is overtaking your life and you cannot cope, you could try medical help.

Go to your doctor and explain your particular fears and how you react to it. There are medicines that will help to reduce the sense of panic. There are others that will block the onset of the panic attack. But like any other stress-management drug, anxiety-reducing medication does have its drawbacks. Some people may be afraid to take these mood-altering drugs because they feel they'll lose control over themselves.

If taking medicines of this nature worries you, tell your doctor who may be able to prescribe the lowest dosage needed for the shortest span possible. Discuss possible side effects and be on the alert for slurred speech, or hazy thought, or any of the pointers the doctor may have indicated. Don't hesitate to ring the surgery if you feel disturbed about some reaction to the medicine. This is the wisest thing to do instead of continuing the medicine without question.

Panic Attacks

A feeling of sheer terror has physical symptoms very much like that of the phobic situation – wildly beating heart, perspiration and a feeling that you are losing control of yourself. But such a panic attack, many people believe, may have biological causes. If, for example, you suffer from asthma, hypertension or a heart condition, you may trigger a panic attack because you are afraid of having a recurrence of your physical ailment. And psychological situations like depression or a phobia could also be the cause.

Fortunately there are ways of minimising the effects of such fear. If you feel a sense of panic rising try, deep breathing as a means of relaxation. In tense situations the body's response is to go in for rapid and shallow breathing in which the upper part of the chest expands. Instead of this try deliberately to develop 'diaphragmatic' breathing in which you fill the lower part of your lungs with air so that your stomach seems to be expanding and contracting. This will create a sense of control and relaxation.

Take deep breaths, counting down from ten. Take a long, deep breath and then exhale slowly saying the word *relax* to yourself. Consciously think of any tension in your neck or jaw or forehead, for example, and try to loosen it up. When you have counted down to breath number one resume whatever you were doing before the attack.

Also use this time to dispel negative and self-critical thoughts. Strengthen your confidence in being able to cope by saying to yourself, 'I can manage these symptoms and I can also carry on with the task in hand. I've survived these before and I'll do even better this time.'

There are drugs to help with panic attacks that verge on the paralyzing in effect, and there is a debate about their side effects.

The best remedy is to take healthy practical steps to help yourself:

■ Stay away from caffeine as research has shown that this causes significant increases in fear, palpitations and other feelings of restlessness.

■ Eat a proper diet which can improve your vitality. Try to avoid foods that have added sugar, caffeine, alcohol, salt and artificial additives. Eat more fresh foods and lean meat and fish.

■ Take a fair amount of exercise, because this reduces stress through a natural physical response. The effect of exercise is to give you a feeling of calm and control over your life.

RISK-TAKING

'I could be knocked down by a bus' may be a colloquial phrase but it does highlight the fact that risk is present in almost everything we do, from going shopping to taking on a mortgage, or going swimming to taking up hang-gliding. The nature of the risk one takes on consciously depends on one's personality. Those who relish a challenge may take up a thrill-seeking sport, like downhill skiing. Some people are more adventurous in the way they live – dressing individualistically or being part of a 'fringe group'.

There are other, longer-term choices one makes that can also be deemed risks – getting married, or changing careers. These can actually be more demanding and cause more stress than a short period of scuba-diving in shark-infested waters.

One analysis of the various kinds of risk divides them into categories:

■ Type 1: The highly stimulating, dangerous activities that do not last long and that constitute a physical challenge. Challenges of another nature fall into in this category: decisions to enter politics or public life. People who take part in television games or public competitions have also decided

94

they want to 'chance it'; they are able to risk performing in front of an audience.

■ Type 2: The decision-making that has lasting effects on your life. This could be taking out a mortgage, deciding to have children, or starting to study as a mature student. These are major commitments; the outcome cannot be foretold but they are calculated risks.

In the Eye of the Beholder
Most of us indulge in both types of risks, but lean more towards one or the other. People who find routine tedious, seek novelty and excitement. For them risking death and disability is not nearly as daunting as marriage. Other people tend to be more comfortable with a Type 2 risks; they may have fun investing money or considering the effects of buying a bigger house; these are, in fact, major commitments.

Nobody conforms to the one characteristic. The stuntman for major films is probably happily married with a family. The otherwise meticulous accountant may go on exploring treks in jungles or drive a speedboat. So risk lies in the eye of the beholder.

Productive Risk-Taking
Why take Type 1 risks at all? Many people assume that the thrill-seekers are all brawn and no brain. But if you examine them more closely you will see that it requires great acumen to cross Niagara Falls on a tightrope, to do the Cresta Run, or to sail the Atlantic single-handed. It requires managing difficult situations, taking quick decisions, and calls for independence and resourcefulness. This creates a sense of mastery of new and difficult situations which will stand you in good stead in life.

Dr Frank Farley, a professor of educational psychology at the University of Wisconsin, has studied the attitudes of people who seek excitement and thrills. He classifies them as Type T or Big T (for Thrill) personalities. At the other end of the spectrum are the Little T people – those who prefer to avoid risks and cling to the familiar, but people can be a mixture of both.

'While most people are uneasy with uncertainty, the Big T personality *thrives* on uncertainty,' says Dr Farley. Dr Farley believes that Big T people test themselves again and again and can handle crises better than Little T people who shrink from risks.

'The Big T personality has less fear and anxiety... and would experience less stress in unavoidable crises. That enables then to keep their cool and make the right decision under pressure,' says Dr Farley. 'The Big T's are self-motivated. They're more creative. And one major facet of creativity is embracing novelty and uncertainty. So they do well in unprecedented situations that require creative solutions.'

This is a selection of guidelines from Dr David Viscott's book:

■ Don't let fear, anger, hurt, guilt or depression impel you take a risk. These emotions should be dealt with independently and not tackled through a hasty move.

■ Don't take on a 'dare' just to prove something to yourself or to others.

■ Do have a goal in mind. A risk taken without a clear sense of purpose is trouble from the start.

■ Don't combine risks unnecessarily.

■ Do be aware of what is at stake and the losses involved. If you don't anticipate the loss, you don't understand the risk.

■ Do list everything that can go wrong, and why. This way you will be able to foresee the problems.

■ Do ask questions. It is better to appear a little stupid than to make a big mistake.

■ Don't rush. Plan to set the appropriate amount of time aside for your task.

■ Do make a timetable. A schedule not only allocates the time, it persuades you that your plan is working.

■ Don't pretend that you're not afraid if you are. Only fools do not fear danger. If the fear won't go away, perhaps you are risking too much.

■ Do act decisively. Once you have decided that the time is right act on it.

■ Don't ignore problems. Attend to them, they will not go away of their own accord.

■ Do take time to correct mistakes. Even when you have embarked on your venture, mistakes can be rectified.

■ Don't give up too soon. Have patience and perseverance.

■ Don't hold on forever. If you know you've lost make a clean break.

To Risk or Not to Risk

Even the most conservative and stable amongst us are faced with questions that require prompt answers – risk having a tooth extracted or hoping the pain will subside. Or it may be a double-or-quits situation. Dr Viscott's checklist includes the following to help clearer thinking:

■ What is the object of the action?

■ Is it necessary?

■ What do I need to know before I start?

■ Who can give me the information?

■ Can I achieve my goal thorugh another route?

■ How much can change because of this action?

■ What can I lose?

■ Is the potential loss greater than the potential gain?

■ What can I do to prevent the loss or harm?

Positive Risk-Taking

Very often there is a mismatch between your particular environment and your personality. A Big T personality may be caught in a routine job with little stimulation and the opposite may happen for a Little T person, creating frustration for both. *Productive* risk-taking in such a context can help to reduce the stress of being in an inappropriate job. It can also lead to outstanding achievements in business, sports, science and the arts, says Dr Farley. *Destructive* risk-taking, on the contrary, is an unsuccessful way of handling the stress of being trapped – matrimonially, occupationally, financially. These negative risks may mean your drinking, gossiping, gambling, shoplifting or other unhealthy or anti-social pursuits.

Dr Farley says the body cannot distinguish physically between a 'bad' thrill or a 'good' thrill. The choice is yours: choose positive, extracurricular activities that fulfill your need for stimulation like sports, dancing, long-distance running rather than the destructive side of that same stimulation – fast driving, drinking, stirring up trouble.

Little T personalities may be perfectly happy and lead satisfied lives says Dr Farley. They do not feel the need to venture their luck. 'Don't forget, the more risks you take, the greater your chances of failure, which could be very stressful – even devastating – if you don't relish risk.' But if you feel you are stuck in a dead-end job, marriage, or any other unrewarding situation you may relieve the tension with a little positive risk-taking.

TYPE A BEHAVIOUR

If you live in a state of continual annoyance and hostility caused by the most mundane of circumstances like a traffic jam then you possibly also view the world as being in opposition to yourself. You could then be classified as a Type A personality who, research has shown, reacts to stress by trying to accomplish more and more in less and less time.

Type A behaviour is characterised by impatience, aggression and hostility. It has been shown to have links to heart disease and can be as hazardous as smoking, high blood pressure or high cholesterol.

The 'Hot Reactor'

Competitive, time-driven, mistrustful Type A's have a nervous system that is on red alert all the time. This makes the body release norepiphrine and other stress-related hormones which in turn triggers production of blood fats that cling to the artery walls and reduce the amount of oxygen being supplied to the heart.

Norepiphrine is a 'struggle' hormone. If you re-live your anger through the day you prolong the effects of the hormone and the harm you do to yourself.

So realize first that a perpetual antagonism to the world will only harm your health. The next step is to realize that you can change. Dr Meyer Friedman, one of the cardiologists who first identified Type A behaviour in 1959 says people can learn new techniques for coping with their reactions. Only 12.9 per cent of Type A people who changed their behaviour had a second heart attack within four and a half years, while 28.2 per cent of the Type A's who did not undergo couselling suffered a second attack.

Dr Virginia Price, a psychologist working with people who have had heart attacks at the Meyer Friedman Institute in San Francisco, says the key to improving reaction to stress is to 'change what you can change, avoid what you can avoid and begin the process of accepting what you can and can't change as a reality.' She says many Type A's who originally assumed that you had to be aggressive to get ahead, said that they had become more successful after modifying their counter-productive behaviour.

She recommends practising Type B behaviour, starting with it consciously while you are driving, since driving seems the most common trigger for Type A behaviour. She says Type A's should first force themselves to drive in the slower lane on the roads.

Here are her other tips:

■ Avoid situations that provoke you. Rearrange your schedule to minimize the number of provocations – shop at offpeak hours if waiting annoys you.

■ Trim your commitments. Don't take on too many obligations. Your natural reaction may be to try to do as much as you can, but resist. Time management and delegation are other useful skills.

■ Get rid of the battle armour. Replace 'AIAI' (anger, impatience, aggravation, irritation) with 'ASAS' (acceptance, serenity, affection, self-esteem). Practise this transfer over and over again.

■ Don't expect perfection from yourself, or from others. Learn to appreciate yourself for what you are, rather than what you accomplish. And do not start on a critical footing with others.

■ Learn to relax. People who have been addicted to adrenalin all the time, do not know what it feels like to relax. Walk more slowly. Don't interrupt others in mid-sentence. Think about your reaction before you explode and then try to control your impatience.

■ Put things in perspective. Most of the everyday hassles, you will soon realize, are not worth having a heart attack for.

A new attitude may cut your risk of heart attack in half – and give you a chance to achieve some happiness and peace.

WORRYING

Much energy can be wasted worrying about events that may never happen, but on the other hand it is not a waste if you take action on what is troubling you. This may lead you to decisions to give up smoking, have a cervical smear, or ring up your mother with whom you have had an argument.

The Red Queen was very wise when she advised Alice in 'Through the Looking Glass' to do her worrying in advance. When the real trouble came along, she would be ready to deal with it calmly.

This is one way of preparing yourself positively. Plan for the expected problem and how you will deal with it should you fail. So if you are trying to get a mortgage and your request is rejected, make alternative plans in advance. The rehearsal will help.

Like a child's cup and ball game, worry seems be to be on the end of a piece of elastic – the more you push it away from you the more it comes back. It is not the worry itself, but the impulse to set it aside that may create the problem. Every time you try to set it aside it keeps coming back.

In this case professor of psychology, Dr James Pennebaker, recommends that worriers give expression to their problems, and talk and discuss them with friends. He believes it helps if you also find a creative outlet to take your mind off your woes – draw, paint or play a musical instrument.

Dr Pennebaker also instructs them to put it down on paper. He asked participants in his research to spend a certain amount of time each four or five days writing about their most upsetting traumas. He found that this had a positive impact on their health. It increased their immune function and, over time, reduced their blood pressure.

Writing about your worries helps you to assimilate them. The very act of putting pen to paper requires you to organize and marshal your thoughts. Twenty minutes a day is probably sufficient; it may take days or weeks for the technique to work but the worries will ease.

The Worry Period

Traditionally all cultures have offered safety valves like the Turkish 'worry' beads, or the rosary. This is a way of creating a time for contemplation. Similarly you could schedule a worry period into your day, rather than living in a state of continuous worry. Use these four steps:

■ Keep half an hour aside, preferably at the same time and place. Postpone all your preoccupations to that one time.

■ If you start to feel anxious about something, identify the real issue and file it away to be tackled during the worry period.

■ Dislodge the worrisome thought by focusing on the task in hand. Concentrate on doing that well.

■ Use the scheduled worry period to work intensively on your woes. Make out a kind of balance sheet. Write the debit (the problem) on one side, the credit (actions to solve) on the other. This practical step will help clearer thought. Remember to keep to the solutions you have listed, you'll use them again.

It also helps if you determine which worry period activity – worrying or problem-solving – is better for you. Each has its place and neither is better than the other.

Have confidence in yourself. Think of the worst possible outcome and you will see that you have probably encountered and tackled that kind of situation before. If you haven't, then think of possible ways to remedy the situation, not worry about it.

3

MEETING THE CHALLENGE OF LIFE'S MAJOR STRESSORS

Change ■ Divorce and Separation

Elderly Parents ■ Grief

Hospitalization and Illness ■ Marital Conflicts

Money Worries ■ Moving House

Retirement ■ Unemployment

CHANGE

It is a truism that the only constant factor in life is change and as such we should all be able to handle it. But this is not so – we often find change distressing.

The degree of stress is proportionate to the degree of change, and also linked to whether the change is of our making. If you are a tenant and are asked to move, this is more disturbing than making the decision to move to a bigger flat of your own accord. If you are reassigned to a new job because of a corporate merger you'll probably feel the stress more than if you chose another job yourself.

Choice is a key element that influences the way you react to change. Psychologists believe there is less stress if you make a choice — even if it turns out to be wrong – rather than having it made for you. It is also better to make a wrong decision instead of being paralysed by the fear of making decisions. But if you do make an inappropriate choice don't keep blaming yourself. It adds to an already difficult situation.

Research has also shown that if you face a change for the better that you did not actually initiate – your boss quits and you get promoted – don't expect the promotion to do wonders for your morale. This kind of positive change (through an external cause) does not always offer as significant a boost to mental health as change intitated by yourself.

If you have to cope with a new situation that you do not like,examine your perspective on the event. Don't indulge in:

■ 'Awfulizing' – seeing the situation as a catastrophe.

■ 'Shoulding' – ascribing blame to yourself or others or making needless demands.

■ 'Rationalizing' – telling yourself you don't care.

You'd do better to focus on the action you can take. For example, the worst has happened to you: you have lost your job. To mitigate the trauma of the event try 'functional thinking'.

■ I'd like not to have lost my job.

■ I'd like to get another one.

■ I'd like to do this with relative ease, but if it takes longer and it's difficult to find one, I'm not going to put myself down because of this.

Transitions

We talk about major life changes being the cause of significant levels of stress. The highest rated is the death of a spouse which is a terrible loss for the bereaved person. The untimely deaths are the most painful; if a person has been seriously ill or is elderly, the fact of their leaving the family is generally more accepted than a sudden loss.

Do not rush the grieving process. It is foolish to try to set limits on it. Weather the pain and take small steps to fill the void. It is also unwise to start searching for a substitute. Other people may be able to fill only some of the roles your spouse played in your life. And have faith in yourself to endure the sorrow, even if your relationship was full of conflict and you are burdened by the guilt of not being able to say you are sorry. Reflect on the past and you will soon see you have an ability to put things in perspective.

Transition, of course, means change. The impact of that change has less to do with the event itself – having a baby, or retiring from your job – as with the way the change alters your many roles as spouse, employee, offspring or friend. According to Dr Nancy Schlossberg, a transition can even be a non-event such as realizing you will never get promoted or that you are not able to conceive.

How well you handle that transition, says Dr Schlossberg, depends on your resources in four areas. She suggests you should take advantage of your assets and try to make up for any shortcomings in the following categories:

■ Situation.
Examine your reaction to see if it is:
Positive/negative
Expected/unexpected
Present at a good/bad time
Voluntary/imposed
Sequentially in the beginning/middle/end
Personally created/reaction to external development

■ Self.
Ask yourself if you have:
Previous experience in coping
Belief in the possiblilty of other options
Optimism/pessimism

■ Support.
Consider your resources:
Financial
Emotional
Family
Friends
Colleagues

■ Strategies.
See what you can devise to:
Change the situation and its implications
Manage the stress

'By systematically sizing up transitions and our own resources for dealing with them,' Dr Schlossberg says 'we can learn how to build on our strength, cut our losses – and even grow in the process.'

DIVORCE AND SEPARATION

Only the death of a spouse ranks higher on the stress scale than divorce and separation. The latter also signify a kind of death — that of a relationship, with the accompanying emotional loss and added burdens of guilt, anger and betrayal. Like a bereavement, divorce creates major changes – in living arrrangements, finances and contact with children. And, depending on one's circumstances, one becomes uncertain of which role to play – the aggrieved or the virtuous, the unfeeling spouse or the martyr.

The Emotional Avalanche

Divorce differs in its effects from that of a death in the family because in the latter people gather round you to give you support. 'Your self-image doesn't suffer,' says Dr Constance Ahrons. But with a divorce one may reluctantly have to take stock of one's life.

'Take a middle-aged woman whose husband has left her for a younger woman,' says Dr Ahrons. 'Like a widow, she feels the stress of living alone, possibly combined with feelings of growing old and watching her children leave home. She may have to face new career demands. But combined with all that is the added humiliation of being publicly rejected for another.'

Then there is the wrangling over money, property and children, adding up to an avalanche of distress which could be much greater than the stress of losing a spouse.

While separation and divorce are never easy, there are ways of preserving your self-esteem and not going bankrupt emotionally or financially. These are practical steps you can embark on when you have realised that your marriage is, in fact, over.

Divorce is not something that happens out of the blue, it evolves through the disintegration of a relationship. Each marriage is different. Some couples know that the break is for them because life apart could not possible be worse than life together. But for many the decision is not that easy to make, and that is an agonising situation to be in.

One approach to decide *if* you should get a divorce is to ask *why* you are considering the break.

The answers may fall into four categories:

■ Divorce as a rational solution. To undo an unhappy situation that is not likely to improve.

■ Divorce as a stress-related response. Marital unhappiness may not be the cause here at all, but some external factor, like a serious illness in the family. This may impose inordinate stress on one partner who copes by opting out of the marriage.

■ Impulsive decisions. Most common of these are those initiated by jealousy – a woman divorces her husband to woo him away from another woman. This strategy generally fails leaving the impulsive partner raging for years.

■ Decisions encouraged by others. Professionals, like marriage counsellors, may advise divorce if the marriage appears to be causing extreme stress.

Coming out on Top

Seeking a divorce is a highly-charged issue. 'You can start by asking yourself 'Am I divorcing the person or the marriage?',' says Dr Ahrons. 'Many adults, married only a year or two, for example, split up because they realise they made a wrong choice.' They get out of the relationship before they have committed themselves too much to it.

The other option is to think seriously about your motivation to continue and invest more emotion and commitment in making your marriage work. This take a great deal of introspection and self-knowledge.

A Survival Kit

You will almost certainly be left with a maelstrom of conflicting emotions, most of them negative, for divorce is a hydra-headed antagonist. Most significant of all probably will be loneliness and loss of a sense of purpose and motivation. Don't wait till the marriage is officially over to nurse your bruised psyche back to health. If you are to survive with your sanity and self-esteem intact your task will be to grapple with your emotions one at a time. Talk to RELATE otherwise also known as the National Marriage Guidance Council, or the National Family Conciliation Council, or the Family Welfare Association (See Reference List).

Keep some of these points in mind:

■ Friends make good shock absorbers. Confiding in others is a good way of coping with the shock of 'I can't believe this is happening to me'. Remember also that there is no stigma attached to divorce; that makes it easier to turn to friends for support.

■ Don't hang on to anger. If you do this (it is easier to focus all your anger on your former spouse) you are only delaying dealing with more urgent things – acknowledging the hurt and then attempting to take a balanced view.

■ Grieving is normal and healthy. Both people in a divorce are in a sense bereaved: the person who initiates the proceedings has decided to make the break; the other spouse is left, as it were, in mourning. Because divorce proceedings entail contact between spouses, your grief may continue, but allow it to be present and don't deny it.

■ Don't pretend your 'ex' does not exist. Divorce does not sever all ties. You may have shared a great deal, particularly if you have children. Dr Ahrons says that a new relationship can be built, similar to the one we have with former suitors or old

111

school friends. 'It's unhealthy to have been married to someone and to have children together and then pretend they don't exist. Denying the relationship is like tearing 20 chapters out of the middle of your life and throwing them away.'

■ Give yourself time. Divorce takes longer to get over than a bad haircut. It may be a couple of years before you feel 'whole' again.

■ See the divorce as an opportunity for improvement. This could be a period of growth. No doubt you will have a number of fresh commitments, especially if you have children. But you can also see this as another start.

■ Resist making rash decisions. You may want to flee from your situation by changing your job; or moving to another city. But such impulses should be resisted, they just impose an extra strain. Don't run away, says Dr Ahrons. On the contrary, build on the familiar that provides a sense of continuity.

■ Consider counselling if you feel you cannot manage on your own. If you are reacting to the divorce by turning to alcohol or drugs or suicidal thoughts, think seriously about seeking professional help. Discuss your feelings with your doctor who will be able to recommend help. Divorce or separation usually means that there will also be a single parent with children so there is also a place for organizations such as Gingerbread. (See Reference List)

Try Conciliation

Thelma Fisher is the Chair of the National Family Conciliation Council (NFCC) which reports that about a third of those who used the NFCC in 1987 resolved every issue and another third partly resolved the issues. Of the remaining third, two thirds did not agree, less than a third received guidance only and a small proportion reconciled.

She says that perhaps the most important feature of reconciliation is the help it can give to parents to tackle the needs of their children. 'Instead of competing over who should have 'custody' and who 'access', parents can begin to plan their children's lives co-operatively so they can see as much of both parents as possible with as little conflict as the parents can manage. Conciliators can help them to understand their children's needs for clear explanations of what is occurring, for reassurance about their continued security and for an assurance of contact with whichever parent leaves the home.'

Thelma Fisher cites American researcher Dr Judith Wallerstein who calls this 'loving permission' and says it it the greatest contribution that the parents can give to the mental health of their children. 1989 will have seen the 10th anniversary of the work of the NFCC with 50 Family Conciliation Services linked to the national council. These can be approached by couples before separation or divorce or aftertwards.

The less the legal profession are involved the better for all parties. The NFCC Conciliators invite couples to meet together in an informal atmosphere instead of appearing in a formal court and then negotiate to find common ground and a solution acceptable to both. The Conciliator is trained to help achieve this with support which is practical. They can only have preliminary discussions about finance and property which have to be handled by solicitors in the end usually.

ELDERLY PARENTS

Old age befalls each one of us, but most people today are living longer than ever before. The scenario of a chronically sick, younger person at home, whose needs often parallel those of an elderly parent, is also a reality for many families. This trend, combined with the disappearance of the nuclear family as the social norm, can place elderly people on the fringe of the family rather than being an integral part of it, should the need arise.

113

Many older people are perfectly capable of looking after themselves, especially if both husband and wife survive. But we do know that women live longer than men and so some of us have to consider looking after our mothers if they are not able to look after themselves. And more often than not the burden falls largely on the women in the family.

Caring for an elderly parent can mean putting them in a residential home, if this is the option you most wish for them. But what about their view? It can mean having a 'granny' flat, if you have the resources to do this with your own home. It can also mean arranging for them to live nearby, have 'meals on wheels' or a home help visit them. The way you care for them depends on your relationship with them, your finances and your concern for them.

Contemporary society, with its preoccupation with youthfulness, can often overlook the tremendous benefits that a grandparent can bestow on the family. He or she can endow the family with a sense of place and purpose, with continuity and a perspective that is to be valued. On the other hand, a parent who is ill, debilitated or handicapped can prove to be an enormous strain and can only be looked after with specialist attention.

Ideally one should take a long-sighted view of one's parents and recognise that they may need looking after in later life. If one of them has kept poor health, or has a chronic condition, you are in a sense forewarned. Do not let the decision come as a surprise to you. Plan their years so that they know where they might be: within a short walk of you, in striking distance by car, near the shops and the doctor, or visited by grand-children who keep them in touch with the younger world.

If, however, such planning has not been considered by you, and the need for care arises, instead of going into a panic, think calmly then get in touch with your local council or Social Security services or one of the national bodies who will advise not only about the elderly but where you can get help for a sick person at home. (See Reference List, Help the Aged, Age Concern, Pensioners Link, National Association of Carers)

GRIEF

There is a ritual that attends bereavement and grief in every culture and many of these customs have been overlaid by the norms that contemporary society has set. The Irish wake, accompanied by 'keening' may seem to many to be outdated – a formal expression of grief without any real meaning.

Yet meaning there is. Grief is a powerful and lasting emotion that must be given an outlet. Tears are a release and crying eases the burden. Even if you do not cry (tears being regarded by some as a sign of lack of control) you cannot pack up your grief and parcel it away forever. If you do, it may surface again in another form. You need to grieve as a human being and transcend it in your own time.

Grief is an affirmation that you have loved. It is not a negative emotion. We should not expect people to 'snap out of it' and be back to normal in a couple of months. It could be lifetime's relationship that has been severed and it will take more than a few months for the bereaved person to adjust to the loss.

Historically we accept that people raise monuments to grief, like Queen Victoria for her beloved Albert. The Taj Mahal is the supreme example of the enduring love of a Mughal Emperor for his young wife. To remember the dead with affection is part of tradition. To feel guilt or think ill of them is not allowed. Yet many people in mourning feel guilty. They may become obsessed with memories of little ways they were unkind to the dead person, or feel anger and betrayal at having been left behind. Yet when they have emerged from their sorrow they will be able to put things in perspective. It is important that they be given the time to do so.

Apart from the desolation and loneliness, you may feel the presence of your departed relative; some people hear their voice or are convinced they saw them walking down the stairs. But they are not going crazy; psychologists say such sensations are common in bereavement. There can also be physical reactions to bereavement, You may suddenly feel symptoms that mimic the final illness of the loved one. A talk with your doctor and a good examination will probably convince you that there is nothing wrong with your health, and relieve the stress at least on that score.

There has been some research on the impact of bereavement on the immune system. Although there is no conclusive evidence so far, some studies have indicated that people who lose a spouse are more likely to develop serious illnesses themselves in the year after their loss.

Even if the exact reason for ill health in a bereaved person is not known, there are still sound reasons for taking extra good care of yourself. You will have already been through traumatic and tiring times. So keep these points in mind:

■ Eat regular, nourishing meals. If you have a relative with you, say you cannot feel the motivation to cook for yourself, and that you would appreciate some help.

■ Try to take some exercise, or go out for a walk. Exercise is a proven tonic.

■ Try not to drink to calm yourself, or to rely on tranquillisers.

One of your greatest needs will be for company and support. You may not want too many people around you, but you will certainly need their emotional support. In more traditional countries like India, there are a number of ceremonies, performed at intervals after the death, at which relatives gather to comfort the family. By western custom the reception after the funeral is more of a social occasion and can signify that the bereaved are now left to manage on their own. The Indian custom allows the family to gather and help in the psychological unwinding of the bereaved. People are seldom left to feel that they are alone in their sorrow.

Relatives and friends rally round at the time of a death. They can stand by you for a while, and if you show signs of 'coping well' they feel you have regained your composure and can manage own your own. Ironically, it is after a couple of months that your real need for support will emerge. At that time you should not feel reluctant to call on your friends for support. Talk to them about your loss, your feelings and cry if you want to. Tears provide emotional release and may even wash away some of the chemicals that stress builds up in our bodies.

If you feel you need professional help, see your doctor. You can also contact Cruse, a voluntary organisation which offers help and counselling for bereaved persons. It has branches all over the UK and its counsellors are available for people to talk to, or for visits to the home. Cruse has a support network for people to meet and to help them regain an interest in social activity. It offers personal and confidential advice, practical information and a useful set of publications. (See Reference List)

HOSPITALIZATION AND ILLNESS

A few days before his 60th birthday, Harry had a heart attack. Not a massive one, but cause enough for hospitalization. His wife, children and grandchildren, not ones to let the little matter of heart disease get in the way of a family celebration, persuaded an understanding nurse or two to look the other way while they smuggled a cake and party hats into his side ward. A patient with a broken leg in the next bed and 21 relatives helped Harry celebrate his birthday – and temporarily forget about his ailing heart.

No one would be so naïve as to imply that hospitalization can always be turned into a party. Treatment for illness or injury is inherently stressful. But a stint in hospital doesn't have to be all doom and gloom. Every effort should be made to make it a pleasant time – someone else is doing the work anyway so enjoy the break.

Children face much more fear than adults. This is worsened when their parents cannot cope with the strain of having a child in hospital. So, if there is a prospect of your child going to hospital, you could do some homework to get acquainted with what lies ahead. (See Reference List)

Taking the Fear and Anxiety out of your Hospital Stay

Always remember you are going into hospital to get better. Secondly, fear is often the result of not knowing the facts and the prospect of facing the unknown – that is why we all fear the dark. By getting as much information about what is going on you will reduce fear and improve control over your situation. Medical staff help you heal yourself so make it clear from the start you regard your stay as a partnership. Research from the World Health Organization shows that nurses play a key role in how you mend. The more you are at ease through their help, perhaps before an op, the better you will undergo it and the faster you will recover. This holds true for conditions as varied as hernia, cardiac catheterization, and minor gynaecological surgery. Patients who know more about their condition and treatment have less post-op pain and need fewer painkillers and sedatives.

■ Nurses are your primary contact and have seen it all before so make good friends with them.

■ Read up on your condition and ask questions. (See Reference List, Hospital)

■ Questions before admission include – why admission? What are the risks? How long in hospital and recovering? Are there any alternatives? What about a second opinion? How long is the waiting list?

■ Since you are likely to be away for more than a few days for a planned admission remember to do the things you would do about the house if you were going on holiday! Once you are in, don't forget to ask how you will be affected, even by the most minor things such as an injection if you have never had one

118

before. If you can get to a shower or the loo on your own two feet, then do so. Bedpans and bed-baths are no longer de rigeur, unless you are absolutely prostrate when you will probably welcome the convenience of their incovenience!

■ Pain management has improved dramatically in recent years. If your complaint is a potentially long-term one then ask about techniques used by the medical staff to help patients. Body and face massages can be an important part of an armoury which should include mental relaxation as well as drugs. One way to relax is to let your jaw go slack with your mouth partly open – let your lips slacken and your tongue rest in the bottom of your mouth. Then breathe easily and deeply. Don't think!

■ Unlike Harry, organize your friends and relatives to call in. Most hospitals welcome individuals who pop in through the day and night provided they are helping not hindering. They are a great boon to get you glasses of iced water, fix your pillow and be ready to remain quiet without being embarrassed. Have a little routine of things written on a list so they do not have to ask you, and write out your daily routine including your relaxation and nap times. This will also make them feel less helpless because they will be helping you.

■ Try to get up and about as soon as you are allowed, even if it is a bit painful because you may be stiff. Hospital staff will not let your over-exert yourself too soon but they know it is better for you to be on the move rather than immobile on your back.

■ Finally, make sure you have your instructions for convalescence clearly written down on your discharge. It will help you recover faster and make the return home a smoother process.

MARITAL CONFLICTS

The object in marriage, according to myth, is to wed a mate

119

who blends perfectly with your personality and temperament. Presumably, once this miracle occurs, you can switch on to auto-pilot and live happily ever afterwards.

In reality, conflict and discord are bound to arise some time after the wedding cake has been cut. It does not take a major calamity such as the loss of a job or a blow like infidelity to put strain on a relationship. Everyday stresses can create considerable friction and fireworks, especially if you and your spouse are unable to discuss the most trivial of issues without acrimony. You need to develop the skills needed to cope with stresses relating to money, sex, children and shared responsibility in the home.

Bickering and Your Blood Pressure

Marital conflict, unless properly handled, can also jeopardise your physical health. University of Michigan studies of 696 men and women over 12 years showed that an inability to express anger, combined with marital stress, can double the risk of death for people with high blood pressure. Venting your anger on the spot or holding it in both increase stress. If you wait for anger to subside and then discuss the problem rationally (reflective coping) this is easier on your health because it restores a sense of control over the situation and helps to solve the problem. (See Index, anger)

■ Take care if you are a woman in the 30–44 age group as, if you suppress your anger or feel guilty, this group is more prone to higher blood pressure. This applies even more so to women aged 45–69. Keeping your cool may also help to improve your immune system and make you less susceptible to opportunistic infections.

How to do it:

■ Count at least to 10 and preferably go away before you come back to discuss the heart of the argument.

120

■ Look at *how* you argue – marriage counsellors say that much of the time it is not the children or the dog which appear to cause the argument but the way people communicate. Don't blame and don't placate – both can backfire later. You may need to think back to whether you communicated badly with your parents or teachers and friends at school.

■ Blamers should avoid saying the other party is wrong and put the stress on saying that they feel 'a little hurt....' Placators should not hide a problem by pretending everything is fine – they should say what is bothering them. Super reasoners should avoid giving the logical answer or solution that fail to realise that other have feelings.

■ Separate the issue from the person and keep the argument to the present and do not drag up the past. If you keep a scoreboard and bring it out every time, then you will always both end up as losers.

MONEY WORRIES

The technological leap between money under the mattress and the high street bank vault does not change how we feel about money – stressed. Surveys show the majority of us feel anxious, depressed or angry about money. The most troubled of us suffer more headaches, fatigue, insomnia. The root of this is a fear of how we will manage without enough money. Concern about unemployment, inflation, possible divorce and surviving on a low pension in old age, all add to money stress. Control and knowledge are two keys to reducing money stress.

■ Draw up a budget for food, clothes, transport, household payments. Do not confuse this routine with an austerity budget. It will help you avoid the latter by pinpointing where you waste money unnecessarily.

■ Make a five-year rolling plan, and this will pay dividends when it comes to buying a car, moving house, starting a new pension plan. The next logical step is to hold family budget meetings – if the phone bill is costing a fortune the users may need to help pay or desist.

■ With the increase in the value of property in recent years it is now possible for individuals to be sitting on a pile of money which has all kinds of financial implications for your potential money-raising as well as retirement plans. More people than ever before may need to consider finding a financial adviser. This may range from an accountant to look at your tax returns to a financial consultant. But be careful to make sure that they do not have a direct financial interest in what they suggest you do with your resources.

■ Things will go wrong so you should always keep something by for that rainy day. It takes the financial pressure out of a flood in the winter. Insurance will take even more pressure off you. It may be painful to pay it out each year but that is the only time it is expensive – when you need it it is cheap. This emergency fund is quite separate from your long-term savings fund which is for your child's wedding or your retirement plan. This kind of security really does reduce stress.

■ If you are a bad saver then use one of the many deduction systems whereby a certain amount of your income goes automatically into a savings account. It is the regularity of it which is important, however much you can afford.

Weathering the Worst

If the bottom falls out of your financial planning because of some totally unforeseen disaster, or you find yourself getting into debt through credit cards or re-mortgaging:

■ Don't blame yourself or indulge in 'if onlys'. Feel sad or upset but no more.

■ Remember, if it is somebody else's money, say the bank's, then they are the one's who need to worry not you. So there is always room for negotiation about repaying the bills and there are plenty of advice centres of different kinds to help you work out repayment of energy bills or mortgage repayments. They will also advise you of your rights, and, since they see the fine print every day, they know where the loopholes are. It helps to take early action.

■ Moneyholics do exist. They can cause themselves a lot of stress trying to earn more and more when they do not really need it. If you are one of them, think whether there may be more satisfaction to be gained from doing some community work or devoting some of your spare time to a hobby that pays you nothing in cash but a lot in kind. Earning friendship when you do not need extra money can be very rewarding.

MOVING HOUSE

There isn't a survey about stress that does not put moving house high on the list of events that can cause trauma. The older you are, the more stressful it may be. Planning and enjoying the move should be your priorities. The reason it upsets us is because it changes our routines and the security of our surroundings. You should expect to be a little depressed or feel a sense of loss but remember to think about the things you are gaining. This is even more important if the move is connected with a change of job or even unemployment. While you should use it as an opportunity to throw things out, remember that the adult equivalent of the child's teddy bear means maintaining continuity with the past.

This is yet another reason for making a move gradually, by planning as far ahead of time as possible. Get to know your new neighbourhood in advance. That is part of drawing up a list of what you need where you live at the moment, and making sure you know where the equivalent is in your new place, whether it is schools, doctors, corner shops, libraries or the town hall information service. That list habit you should by now be developing. It takes a little time but saves a lot.

If you have not moved before, ask a friend to go through with you how they did it. It is amazing how people pack up all the kitchen last when in fact they need a skeleton kitchen service first! It may be better to enjoy the liberty of takeaway food for a few days and have time off from the kitchen while you get bedrooms comfortable and the video and television working under full steam so they take the strain, not you. Holidays are mini-moves and they are a good model to copy. Finally, the move has to bring new things into your life, including making friends by asking your neighbour for that apocryphal half cup of sugar – so treat it as an adventure which will take time to unfold.

RETIREMENT

Your golden years. In theory retirement does sound golden. Freedom, glorious freedom to do as you please, with no boss, no children to bring up. The aim should be to make your retirement years, sometimes as much as a third of your life, your most enjoyable.

Without forethought retirement can also produce an extra 50 hours a week of not knowing what to do with your time. You may feel a loss of self-esteem because you have no one to work with or supervise, or guilt at being unproductive, or insecurity about your health or money. Wives and husbands suddenly find they do not like each other around too much, giving point to the old maxim, 'twice as much husband, half as much money'. A husband at home for lunch is no longer a pleasant surprise but an annoying interruption in a wife's routine of shopping and meeting friends for a break from work at home. The most likely candidates for a successful transition, from work to permanent leisure, are those who keep good health, have enough money to manage and are prepared to see a new phase opening up in their personal development.

Retirement Planning

Experts differ about how long men, for example, survive after retirement. If you retire from a stressful job and adjust well your health may improve. One estimate of average life expectancy at 65 is about 14 years. To avoid potential stress, and linked physical ailments beyond the normal ones associated with aging, long-range planning is essential. A step-by-step plan avoids the fixation with all the unknowns of the future that can immobilize you mentally and physically. Those who say they stay in bed because there is nothing to get up for need to make sure there is a reason for each stage of their day.

One of the most important moves you can probably make before retirement is to get nearer to your children or relatives. You can also get them to come nearer you. Many times an elderly person ends up alone in a big house or flat. With a little investment it is often possible, before retirement, partly to convert where you live so that there is room, with clear independence, for an unmarried son or or daughter or grandchild to live, or married children whose own children are beginning to make their own way in the world. The cost of such a conversion will pay for itself by a pooling of resources. Even if there is no daily physical help between the two sides there is a major reduction in stress because of the increased physical and mental security.

■ Prepare some new activities and talk to the various pension funds or senior citizen organizations who have good packages on what and how to do it. (See Reference List)

■ Agree with your spouse to have different territories so that you each have mental and physical space – the garden shed is a classic for the man and the wife can help to make it comfortable. If you are single, do not be afraid to develop a romantic attachment but remember too that space remains important particularly if you have ingrained personal habits of a long-time loner.

■ Before retirement begin to develop a network of friends and social acquaintances and plan your campaign of action to achieve this. Pensioners in the United States seem to be very good at doing this, organizing holidays together, retirement towns that are active places not burial grounds. One organization provides access to passenger-carrying freighters so that inveterate travellers can take low budget 'cruises' around the world with all of the friendship and little of the cost of the Queen Mary.

Money

Many fear growing old in poverty. The older generation who saw real poverty during and after the World War II also have a fear of not being buried properly. State pensions now guarantee some form of safety net but it is clear to all that they are not sufficient to live comfortably. Somewhere around 75 per cent of your previous income is needed to maintain your standard of living. Pension planning must happen before the event, while you are still earning well and certainly 10 years before retirement. That includes working out a budget, taking account of inflation, but also realizing that you may not need two cars, may need less insurance and less expensive holidays. Apart from selling a house bigger than your needs, and keeping the difference as a cushion, if you have family and friends you may also want to spend a number of months with them at their expense!

Remember too that there are a range of benefits available for pensioners under social security regulations which you should know about so that you can take advantage of them and not find you have missed out because of poor planning on your tax thresholds or how much money you have invested.

A Second Career

There has been a sea change in the jobs market. There is growing evidence that over the next decade the number of jobs, particularly part-time ones, available for the older in society will grow in the service sector. This is partly because of the fall off in the birth rate and the availability of young people for work. But it is also accompanied by a change in recruitment by major companies such as supermarkets. They see the older generation as being quite able to do part-time work and as being more reliable and indeed honest. The important thing is that the part-time job allows a transition between the level at which you are working. But you must also seek information from an advice centre about how a job will affect your tax status. And do not start to look around for ways of making a million through doubtful schemes which claim to turn your pot of gold into a barrel. Play safe with your money.

As for this second job, it may be a modified form of the work you have done all your life. The insurance salesman is the obvious person for this one. If you are handy at repairing appliances in an age when it is notoriously difficult to get things repaired you might want to prepare a workshop at home in the spare bedroom to do neighbourhood jobs. To boost this you will find there are a range of college and evening courses available to help you refine your skills as well as introduce you to a whole new range of friends. Newspaper librarian Barbara Newcombe moved closer to her children and grandchildren. She bought herself a computer, learned how to use it and then began collecting contacts amongst publishers to offer them book indexing. She is now building up her interest in archives and genealogy.

Keeping Your Self-esteem

Whether you worked as a chairman of a company or the

doorman who stopped undesirables getting in to see you, people will see you in a different light after retirement. The important thing is how you see yourself and your innate worth. The earlier planning we have talked about will influence the maintenance of your self-esteem.

The solution often lies in making sure that your new activities fill the vacuum but in a different fashion. One pensioner, Robert Kennedy, has found that going to the local school two days a week as a volunteer helper has made him a grandfather many times over through sharing his knowledge, experience and friendship with a new generation of young-sters. But you will also find groups of former employees in the same position as yourself who will be happy to share new activities. There is no good reason why you should ignore the advantages of pensioners' groups, whether for days out or shared buying schemes to keep costs down and get over the problem of not being able to buy in bulk any more.

Keeping busy with new interests is the basic message about retirement. Just remember that you have to work at enjoying yourself – that is part of the fun.

UNEMPLOYMENT

Millions have been hit by unemployment in recent years. It is the ultimate in the loss-of-control feeling. The alarm clock to get you up in the morning has no meaning, the worries over meeting regular household payments, the loss of work friends and the satisfaction you got from work itself all hit you at once. The medical evidence that job loss, and indeed the fear of redundancy can affect your health, particularly through stress is well established, whatever governments may say to the contrary.

This is where a rigorous appraisal of your day becomes very important. The story of how difficult it can be to join the job search round need not be told here however. It should be said that you must take action to ensure that you fight against the first stages of shock, denial, the unnerving optimism of the

128

'holiday feeling' followed by anxiety and distress. Because this all combines to lower your mental resistance to day-to-day pressures, it also lowers your bodily resistance to day-to-day physical ailments. The discipline needed to replace the routine of work must also take into account the risks that you may begin to compensate by overeating, drinking and smoking. If you are middle-aged then a clear plan of action is even more important.

Do's and Don'ts:

■ Break the news softly to your partner after thinking it through yourself. There may be anger but at least one of you must cope with it calmly.

■ If you are feeling suicidal send out an SOS. It may be to the Samaritans, your local advice centre, a priest, rabbi or friend. There are lots of professional hotlines available which are anonymous, so use them even if you think that your partner can cope – they may not be able to. Getting your feelings out into the open is usually the most important first step and things begin to fall back into perspective much more quickly than you might think.

At home, everyone is going to be under stress, including your children who are far more vulnerable to the threat of 'doing without', than you think. There is a time and a place and a level at which they must be involved in the implications of what has happened. But it needs to be done carefully after consulting with friend or expert counsellor. If the company you were with has a counselling service for employees being made redundant then you should not feel too proud to use it. It was set up precisely for that purpose.

■ Get out of bed in the morning.

■ Look for a job elsewhere in the same kind of work, and do not rule out a competing company – they may need you!

■ Line up allies in the same position as you. Many new ventures started because two or three friends got together to set up a cooperative, pooled their redundancy money and took advantage of government grants for re-training or enterprise start-ups. Ask your social contact network about job possibilities – many jobs never appear in the job columns. It is not a question of asking them for work but where it may be available.

■ Make looking for a job at least a part-time job in itself. This increases your chances of landing a job and keeps time from hanging heavy on your hands. Keep a good record of everything which you apply for. This does not only help you keep a track of what is going on and give you a sense of your level of effort. It also helps those around you, particularly children, to appreciate how much you are doing to try to help them. They know they can still depend on you and you are not losing your nerve.

■ Consider devoting part of your time to volunteer work. This gets you out of the house every day, it looks good on your job applications and it tells prospective employers that you are not depressed. It also makes you fit into someone else's needs and timetable and gives you a sense of control.

■ Step up your exercise programme – you now have the time and there are usually concessions for the unemployed on membership and entrance fees. Not only will this reduce stress, insomnia and out-of-work blues, it will help you with job applications. You should also give yourself a treat occasionally, not only for the boost it will give you but also because it will stop you going on some mad splurge.

■ Make new friends to replace the ones you have lost at work. They will also be invaluable, if they are also unemployed, in telling how to cope with the 'system'.

■ Keep in touch with developments in your area of work

whether through the library or professional associations. If people know you are out of job they will not expect you to 'pay your share'.

The Hidden Benefits of Losing Your Job

There really is always a silver lining. Losing your job may in fact be the start of a much better job and way of life for you and your family. There are countless instances of people taking up a new interest which becomes very important to them and which they never had the time to explore before. It could turn into a job or it may be the ideal backup, such as painting or gardening, that you can use to keep your equilibrium while you get your life rearranged and re-evaluate what you are all about. That means the validity of your expectations and how, and if, you want to work. This time of reappraisal is a luxury few people ever have.

4

PREVENTING AND TREATING PHYSICAL PROBLEMS

Back Pain ■ Colitis

Coronary Artery Disease ■ Fatigue

Headaches ■ Immunity ■ Insomnia

Sexual Dysfunction ■ Ulcers

BACK PAIN

The dull ache above the hips. The biting twinge in the middle of the back. The soreness around your shoulders that's moved in like an invasion of red ants – and seems about as likely to leave. Eighty per cent of us have backache at one time or another and for millions the pain is as regular as the postman. Rarely is it caused by disease or a structural problem. Much is put down to the muscles, weak perhaps because of a desk job, a constant slouch, extra weight or careless lifting. If it is of that kind, then back pain may also be due to an element of stress.

Stress causes muscles to tighten up. When they are forced to make a sudden movement their rigidity can create a spasm which causes a knot which, in turn, causes more spasms. Constant rigidity over a period may make a muscle lose its elasticity. This can lead to jerky movements and make the muscle more susceptible to injury.

Ways to De-Stress Your Back

Several of the stress management techniques described in this book may help to keep you from turning stressful situations into back pain. Many people respond well to massage (see Index, massage) as a means of relieving pain. A light, stroking massage at home can relax muscles and relieve spasms. Deep breathing techniques (see Index, breathing) are accepted as part of relaxation training. Doctors E. Loehr and Jeffrey A. Migdow offer a routine in their book *Take a Deep Breath* :

1. Keep your eyes closed throughout

2. Begin abdominal breathing using your tummy instead of your chest.

3. Imagine tension leaving your body, like steam or a stream of colour, as you exhale.

4. Imagine relaxation coming in as you exhale.

5. Move parts of your body as you breathe.

6. Imagine your incoming breath travelling to the area of pain and filling it with calmness.

7. Imagine the pain flowing out with each exhalation.

8. Allow yourself, through crying or sighing, to release any emotion related to the pain.

9. Continue steps 5 through 8 for five to 10 minutes.

10. Feel the movement of your breath again.

11. Stretch your arms and legs.

12. Open your eyes when you feel better.

You could combine this routine with other methods, For example you could listen to relaxation and exercise tapes, or try biofeedback as well. (See Index, biofeedack)

A number of studies also suggest that if you look deeper for the stress cause of back pain you may find it in family conflict, a lack of friendship at work or low self-esteem. Therapy can help in this, just as it can help with pscyhosomatically induced eczemas. If you want more information on ways of helping yourself you could contact the National Back Pain Association. (See Reference List)

COLITIS

Colitis can make life a real misery. The most prevalent form is ulcerative colitis – inflammation of the colon lining. When there are flare-ups you may spend much of your time on the loo or in bed, because of severe diarrhoea, sometimes with blood, because the inflamed bowel cannot absorb food. This can lead to weakness and loss of weight. Irritable bowel syndrome (IBS) is not colitis but it strikes 50 per cent to 75 per cent of us at one time or another. To add to the discomfort, constipation alternates with diarrhoea and one can have stomach pains as well. Unlike colitis, which may be hereditary, there is no known cause or associated disease responsible for

135

causing IBS. But stress does aggravate the symptoms. So stress management is one element in the treatment of both conditions.

A Canadian nursing school study of 80 people gave half of them relaxation classes, assertiveness training, tips for communicating better with others, worry control and time management. Worry control is important to stop the fear that you won't be able to cope with colitis when it flares up. If you plan your time to get certain jobs done then, when an attack occurs, you worry less about chores piling up. The study found that the people who practised stress management saw their ailment dwindle while the others, who had not been given the benefit of such management techniques, experienced no improvement.

Hypnotherapy May Help

Dr Edward Taub, an Alabama University psychologist and Dr Alan Ginsberg, director of the gastroenterology clinic at George Washington University School of Medicine, gave hypnotherapy to 25 patients. They were told under hypnosis that they could handle the illness and its symptoms and were given relaxation tips. Half of them benefited. Deep breathing and massage also seem to help. This encouraged people to get to sleep more quickly, increased their sense of control over the pain and induced a state of calm more quickly.

Knowledge about your condition is important, as spelt out in the section on going into hospital. You should also be aware that people with colitis have a higher than usual risk of developing cancer of the colon or the rectum. (See Reference List, Hospital, Going into)

CORONARY ARTERY DISEASE

While high blood pressure, high cholesterol levels, diabetes, being overweight and smoking are the five biggest risk factors that make coronary heart disease the major health problem in many industrialized countries, they do not explain the whole picture. Stress is another very significant, but sometimes hidden, factor.

We certainly seem to face many more stresses and shocks in our twentieth century world than our cave-dweller ancestors would have faced. But it is perhaps the *chronic* stress rather than what one doctor has called the 'sabre-toothed' tigers of modern daily living, which threatens us directly or indirectly by increasing risk factors such as cholesterol levels.

Nervous tension can raise your cholesterol as easily as eating a ham and cheese omelette. Giving up in the face of a stressful event can be as bad for your blood pressure as getting fighting mad. Nor does a low-salt, low-cholesterol diet necessarily cancel out the effect. Some doctors produce evidence to show that acute stress response 'takes the bite out of the heart muscles', overcontracting the small muscle fibres 'until some of them rip', leaving the heart vulnerable to arrhythmias – heart spasms that can cause sudden death.

Pulling the Plug on Stress

You have to get to know yourself and your daily routine if you are to identify those things which stress you in particular — we all operate in different environments.

Identify the three things which you feel are the biggest cause of stress for you – traffic, deadlines or a relationship – and you are well on the way to picking out the others. It is like an overloaded plug in the wall with an adaptor and half a dozen appliances on it – remove three and things are much easier on the system. You need a certain level of effort in what you do. If you feel you are getting a job done at a certain pressure load then you should find that your blood pressure will be fine and your immune system will keep in trim. If you are struggling and feel you are not making headway, then you risk being caught in the 'struggle/defeat' syndrome which will simply increase your stress.

Mastering Stress

Here are seven ways to manage stress and your reaction to it:

■ Don't overreact by making a mountain out of a molehill.

■ Talk yourself down from the brink by using positive self-talk which, instead of complaining, looks at the positive side. People turning up late give you opportunity time to do something else while you wait, rather than complain about their punctuality.

■ Stand back and consider all your options instead of being overwhelmed by one of them.

■ Learn to say no and save yourself trying to do more than you can.

■ Set realistic expectations of yourself and others – excellence is the aim, not perfection.

■ Make friends who will help you in time of need – lend you money, give you a lift, or a bed if you have nowhere to go.

■ Find a relaxation technique which suits you and practise it daily.

Dr Robert Eliot of the Swedish Medical Center in Colorado says that people following the Center's preventive programme can control their blood pressure without medication. Their cholesterol levels drop, they are less anxious, hostile and depressed and have fewer arguments, headaches, back pains and they sleep better. He also says their income has risen as a result of better control over, and so more productive, work.

FATIGUE

Everyone feels tired once in a while. But when you cannot put it down to jet lag or working late, it may be a surplus or a lack of stress. It may in turn be a physical ailment, your diet, sleep habits or mental health.

Check Your Physical Health

Fatigue can be a symptom of disease, so first check with your doctor and make sure you are not suffering from something such as diabetes, anaemia, liver, or kidney problems. If you are clear, it may be your weight (probably a good place to start anyway before suspecting something else). Combine any sensible dieting with exercise and remember walking is still the cheapest and best way to tone the body up.

When you look at your diet also check what sort of mineral and vitamin intake you have. People have different needs at different times of life and in different occupations. Stress uses up certain trace elements, but balance is the order of the day, not a binge on supplements or vitamins. Some of the nutrients we depend on include vitamins B_1 and B_2, pantothenate, vitamin C, chromium, manganese, selenium, potassium, calcium and zinc. Consult with the expert – a doctor or dietician.

Check Your Sleep Habits

Your fatigue may be due to poor sleep. Stick to a regular bedtime and waking-up time. Check whether caffeine, alcohol or other drinks affect your sleep by cutting them out on a trial basis. Some people may need more sleep than others so see if that is true for you. Catnaps during the day won't necessarily make up your loss, but there are many who make a point of having an 'extra' sleep during the day and it works for them. Emotional upsets or worries carry over into rest and disturb it unless you make a positive effort to clear them from your mind before you go to bed. This has to be a positive thing. One way is to think about them and get them into the

139

right perspective so that they are less overwhelming than they would appear.

Check Your Arousal Level

According to one theory, anxiety improves performance until a certain optimum level of arousal has been reached. Then performance deteriorates. If you are not tapping your energy potential you need to increase the challenges or vice versa. Biofeedback (See Index, biofeedback) will help you see whether you are following your internal clock or leading it.

With a good diet, regular exercise and a solid night's sleep behind you, even stress will not rob you of energy.

HEADACHES

Chronic headaches directly brought on by stress are most commonly caused by muscle contraction. These 'tension headaches' afflict people when they transfer their tension to their muscles. Aggravations such as a child dumping the jam all over the carpet, excessive demands at work from a supervisor, cause your mucles in the head and neck to contract. This constricts blood vessels and this is believed to be the main cause of the discomfort.

The first step, therefore, is to tackle the source of the stress rather than reaching for a pill. Research which uses electrodes attached to various groups of muscles of headache sufferers can detect whether normal electrical levels of activity are being exceeded. This method of assessing headache muscle tension shows that generally it is the *frontalis* muscle, across the forehead, which tenses first. However it can also be the muscles in the back of the neck or in the jaw, with the headache eventually working its way up to the head.

You could try some of these tips:

■ Think and work your headache away using progressive

relaxation, deep breathing or stretching exercises to loosen the neck or jaw. A warm bath can also help. (See Index, relaxation, stretching, baths)

■ Keep a daily record of headache episodes and note the feelings, activities, and environmental factors that precede or accompany the pain. By cognitive therapy, learning to understand how thoughts and external factors contribute to headaches, you can begin to change them. If it is a particular job in the office that triggers things then you can analyse whether it is the person making the demand or the actual request itself that is the cause.

■ Once you have identified these causes, you will be able to take steps to make them less capable of affecting you adversely.

Migraines

Migraines are more dramatic than muscle contraction headaches. They are technically considered *vascular* headaches. The causes are still not totally clear but one explanation is that the blood vessels or arteries inside or outside the skull expand, exert pressure on nearby nerves, and so cause the pain. Migraine does run in families and some suggest there is a hereditary connection. Other explanations include an imbalance of chemicals in the body. A migraine attack results when the carotid arteries supplying blood to the brain constrict. To compensate the brain releases neurochemicals to dilate the arteries back to normal. Migraine sufferers seem to experience an over-stimulation so that the arteries overdilate stretching sensitive pain receptors that are wrapped around them.

For the sufferer, the important thing is to try to pinpoint the triggers, perhaps in food or certain kinds of stress. Some studies show that stress three or four days before a migraine episode can be a trigger. There is no generally accepted 'cure' for migraine but stress control may help reduce its incidence. Consultation with allergists has helped many sufferers who then avoid a particular food. You need to check with your doctor about recent advances on the drugs front in this field. But there are also plant derivatives, such as that from the common weed feverfew, which has proved very effective for tackling migraines when taken on a preventive basis. Studies by the Chelsea Physic Garden, London, with Chelsea College, University of London, on feverfew showed statistically extremely high benefits. (See Reference List)

IMMUNITY

People who have gone through tough times sometimes get sick. Those who rise and dominate the challenge of a disease are sometimes able to overcome it. Such would be Bob Champion, the National jockey who fought back and won against testicular cancer. Jessica is the name of a woman who sold her beautiful old home and moved into a small, easy-to-manage flat. But the move was an expensive one and she had to sell some of her old treasured, furniture to pay the removals firm. After only three days in the new flat, with curtains still unhung and packing boxes still to be unpacked she developed a thunderous cough and a temperature. She came down with bronchitis and her illness may well have been related to the stress of moving.

This stress-respiratory illness sequence has been confirmed by researchers over the years. It is also thought that stress may trigger herpes attacks. It is not a direct cause and effect. It is more that the stress weakens the body's resistance and opens the door to the opportunistic infection. What we call 'feeling low and run down'.

Stress – the Last Straw

Modern medicine and the influence of Christian thinking have both tended to split the mind from the body. But new research, called psychoneuroimmunology, has brought together modern scientific expertise to prove what much ancient medicine already knew – that there is a balance between the mind and the body, a *yin and yang*, a healthy mind in a healthy body. The immune system, when operating normally, moves in to attack invading bugs and kill or neutralise them. But it works hand in hand with many other factors – heat, cold, what you eat, the genetic blueprint you inherited, your age and sex, cultural origins, your internal clock and possibly stress.

One theory suggests that stress prompts the brain to trigger the nervous system to release hormones that can jam your immune system. Increase of cortisol secretions, for example, lead to the production of weaker lymphocytes, the cells which are important for immunity. Another study showed that stress-related hormones (specifically epinephrine and nor-epinephrine) appear to block the ability of immune cells to kill cells infected with herpes simplex viruses, such as genital herpes.

Stress weakens the system and opens the door to attackers. While present scientific methods, to quantify the various levels of immune resistance or weakness through deficiences or strengths in the way we think, are inadequate, there is enough evidence to accept the linkage. For most, when stress increases, immunity decreases.

Therefore the antidote is to strengthen the role of the mind in helping to keep the body healthy. By learning to deflect or diffuse stress you may deflect or diffuse disease. A study of students who were part of a relaxation programme showed that antibody activity in their saliva rose as a result.

There is a whole programme to help you 'mentally vaccinate' yourself to improve your immunity by controlling your emotions spelt out in Dr Paul Pearsall's pioneering book 'Superimmunity – Control your Emotions and Improve your Health'. (See Reference List)

INSOMNIA

Counting sheep, hoovering at 3 a.m. with a mug of tea in your hand, are both part of the torture of sleeplessnes. Thirty to 35 per cent of us suffer insomnia in some form and it ranks second after headaches as a cause for going to the doctor. What can one do?

Do some exercise during the day, don't eat a heavy meal in the evening, read a light novel or unwind in front of the television before bedtime. Cut out alcohol, sugar or caffeine during the day or at least after midday.

When it comes to your sleepless bedtime the most important thing to do is relax – intense activity to put yourself to sleep is counter-productive. It increases tension.

■ Try a relaxation exercise.

■ Don't take an alcoholic drink – read, or watch television.

■ Exercising three or four hours before you go to bed will take any pent-up steam out of your body, but such activity when you are actually trying to get to sleep simply stimulates the muscles.

■ Don't raid the fridge. Like the cat, your body may want feeding at the same time every night!

■ Don't take work to bed. The very nature of the material will be telling your mind not to let you drop off to sleep.

Charles Dickens, a noted insomniac, recommended making sure your bed faces the north pole to line up magnetic forces. There may well be something in that. More doubtful was Benjamin Franklin's suggestion that you get up, re-make the bed, walk around naked until freezing cold and then hop back into your warm bed.

Sleeping Pills

The use of drugs such as diazepam (Valium) to help people get to sleep, or indeed to cope with acute depression, is now under very serious review. There have been so many thousands of cases of serious addiction from prescribed drugs which started off as just a small helping hand, that the consumer should have tried everything else before turning to pharmaceutical support.

It is better to react positively to temporary stress because it will vanish when the long overdue cheque drops through the door, or you get through your exam. One young woman who was given a few sedatives to get her through her wedding day stayed on them for years and it destroyed her life.

Having made sure that continuing insomnia is not caused by some physical ailment, and if the guidelines above are not working, another option is sleep restriction. This involves discipline. For one week you keep a log of the amount of time you spend in bed and the time you actually sleep. If the first is greater than the second, then you must only spend the fewer hours in bed. There is no lying in bed, just hoping. The routine is to establish sleep, however little, as 90 per cent of your time in bed, and then increase your 'bedtime' by 15 minutes each night until the insomnia is treated.

Here is a general routine:

1. Lie down with the intention of going to sleep only when you are sleepy.

2. Do not use your bed for anything except sleep – no reading, watching television, eating or worrying in bed. Sex is the only exception and then you follow the instructions again.

3. If you find yourself unable to fall asleep, get up and go into another room. Stay as long as you wish and then return to the bedroom to sleep. Although you should not necessarily watch the clock, you should get out of bed if you do not fall asleep immediately. Remember, the goal is to associate your bed with falling asleep quickly. If you are in bed more than about 10 minutes without falling asleep and have not got up, you are not following this routine!

4. If you still cannot fall asleep repeat step **3**.

5. Set your alarm and get up at the same time every morning, regardless of how much sleep you have had during the night. This will help your body clock acquire a consistent sleep rhythm.

6. Do not nap during the day.

Older People Need Less Sleep

As we get older our sleeping patterns change. We sleep more lightly and require fewer hours. Between the ages of 20 and 50, deep sleep is reduced by 60 per cent, and the number of arousals in the night doubles. Keep in mind that it is normal to sleep less as you get older. You're not suffering from insomnia, unless your sleep patterns have changed dramatically and persistently, or if you are experiencing symptoms such as lethargy, irritability, poor coordination and lapses of attention. If that's not so, then enjoy the fact that your body needs less sleep. Eight hours a night is not de rigeur at all. Use the extra waking hours to your advantage.

SEXUAL DYSFUNCTION

Stress can have a major effect on your sex life and it is put as the cause of as much as 80 per cent of problems surrounding erections in men. Much has to do with the fear of failure and a man's self-esteem. Losing a row with a wife or loss of promotion at work can damage a man's 'manhood' and make erection difficult. Signs of middle-age are another factor, or failure to satisfy a woman, compound the anxiety.

For her part the woman may feel guilt that she is part of his failure to have an erection. If he succeeds, she may fail to respond with her vagina not producing lubricants and she may find that she cannot achieve an orgasm. A similar figure of 80 per cent of problems surrounding orgasm in women are also attributed to stress by psychiatrist Harry Caplan of San Fransisco. The stress can come from various and varied events in life including a frustrated sex life.

The first step to tackle this is to see it all as a health problem and nothing to do with your own personal worth. The James Bond picture of lovemaking is not a reality so you do not need to try to match your performance. Desire changes with age too, so expect changes in your sex life – they are normal not 'problems'. The emphasis can be changed to one of pleasure not performance.

Before you consider consulting a sex therapist you should establish a few facts. If you find that you wake up with an erection, or certain people or images turn you on, then your system is functioning normally. But smoking, through nicotine's effects, can damage your potency so you need to think about that if you are a smoker. Try stopping for three weeks and if you are still unable to have to an erection then it is not the tobacco. The same applies to alcohol. This can also have a physical impact on a man's testicles by reducing them in size. Also check with your doctor in case you are taking medication which may create side-effects, affecting your sex life without your knowing.

Anxiety may also be a cause. If you apply what you have learnt from the various sections of this book properly, you will be able to see if it is the root of your problem. Stress can upset your stomach so there is no reason why it should not upset other parts of your body! Under stress blood flows towards your muscles and away from your penis or from the vagina. Under normal circumstances the sympathetic part of your nervous system kicks in as your sexual excitement mounts but stress can upset the automatic trigger balance and instead restrict the arteries to the genitalia and stop them taking in more blood.

Talking out the problem with your partner is not only useful but it is the obvious thing to do as they are the one you are going to have sex with. Usually therapists recommend that you abstain from sex, and try to talk and caress to set a base for having sex rather than focusing on the act itself. This often lets the genitals 'relax' as much as you, and their function will return. Some recommend a period of three weeks of abstinence from direct sex with half-hour sessions devoted only to foreplay. In the three weeks after that genital and breast touching is allowed, but no intercourse. If this has not worked then you need to consult a sex therapist and contact can be made through your doctor. The National Marriage Guidance Council may also be able to offer help. (See Reference List)

ULCERS

Contrary to popular belief, ulcers are very democratic. They do not select just the 'go-getter' executive types but bestow their favours irrespective of occupation: white, blue or pink collar, or no collar at all. Their ally, stress, it emerges, is equally just. What scientific investigation has revealed, however, is that certain physical factors can influence the susceptibility towards ulcers.

The two main elements are the secretion of gastric juices and the nature of the mucous that lines the digestive tract. But a third element appears in the non-physical category, the way that people *react* to events. A combination of these three can influence the onset of ulcers.

The exact nature of the combination is hard to determine. But what does emerge is that, as a group, people with ulcers seem to experience more anxiety and fear than others when events threaten to disrupt their lives. This means that the physiological reaction to stress, in the release of gastric juices, may interfere with the body's defence mechanism in some way. This could lead to a breakdown in the way the stomach and duodenum protect themselves against acid secretion. Ulcers are the result, accompanied by the burning sensations, pain and bloated discomfort.

One investigation of three different groups of men: kidney and gallstones patients, ulcer victims and normal, healthy

148

men showed that all of them experienced roughly the same amount of potential stressors. Yet the ulcer group differed in some significant ways. They were more likely than their healthy counterparts to view changes in life, like a new job or a transfer to another city, in a negative way. Many tended to be hypochondriac, over-pessimistic and overly dependent. They had a low 'ego strength' (ability not to break under stress) and a higher than average level of alienation from society – a feeling that they had fewer friends and relatives to call on in time of crisis.

Helping the Sensitive Stomach

Psychologist Dr Pamela Walker says that people who have an ulcer can learn stress-management techniques.

Here are a few tips that may make life a great deal easier for sensitive stomachs:

■ Teach yourself. Learn how your body reacts physically to stress, specifically the gastrointestinal system. Also learn how to change a habitually 'worried' thinking system.

■ Talk to yourself. This is cognitive therapy, also called self-talk or self-affirmation, in which you try to think positively instead of immediately reacting in a negative manner. 'Negative thinking tends to be a self-fulfilling prophecy,' says Dr Walker. 'So if you think things will go wrong, you may be more likely to do things that lead to failure... You've got to break the cycle and cognitive therapy does the trick.'

■ Study assertiveness. If you tend to suppress your anger you often communicate it indirectly to others anyway. This lack of ability to relate well to other people denies you the very support that you may need in times of stress. So learn to express your feelings appropriately through studying assertiveness techniques. This will release you from the clutch of unproductive emotions. (See Index, assertiveness)

■ Learn to relax. The opposite of the stress response is the relaxed response. Learn how to operate this antidote by studying meditation or methods of relaxation. (See Index, relaxation)

5

COPING TECHNIQUES THAT DO NOT WORK

Alcohol ■ *Coffee* ■ *Compulsive Shopping*

Nervous Habits ■ *Overeating* ■ *Smoking*

ALCOHOL

Many people think that a drink will help them unwind, and ease the tension they are under. The result may be the quite the opposite. The relaxed feeling that alcohol produces is only temporary. In fact prolonged drinking stimulates excess production of hydrocortisone and other stress-related hormones. This is because the activity of the neurons of a sector of the brain (called the locus coeruleus) is inhibited by alcohol. This triggers off a reaction in another set of brain cells which raises feelings of stress and is directly caused by excess consumption of alcohol.

Many people start to drink heavily as a result of some crisis in their life. It might be an event related to their work; with women it is often linked to marriage or romantic relationships. Such a situation leads people to rely on alcohol to sort out their feelings. But alcohol is really an undependable ally.

If you want to discover whether you are using alcohol as a crutch, ask yourself these questions:

■ Do you drink every day? An occasional pint to relax or celebrate is fine, but relying on it solve your problems is not.

■ Is your consumption such that your blood alcohol levels are significantly raised? A good rule of thumb to determine this is to see if you get through more than one standard drink per hour. This may be a glass of wine, a half pint of light ale or a single whisky or other spirits. Regardless of your size or weight you should realize that your body cannot metabolize more than than the single standard drink in an hour. A faster rate of consumption just creates an overload. In the end your body becomes more and more tolerant of alcohol and requires even greater quantities to achieve a calming effect.

■ Does drinking trigger churlish behaviour? Are you more aggressive physically or in speech; do you tend to get rough with your wife or the family?

152

If you have answered 'yes' to any of the above questions it may be time to stop and evaluate the role alcohol plays in your life.

■ Keep a record of your drinking habits. Make a note of the occasions on which you drank, how much, the circumstances, people present, your reaction to them. If you can identify the people, places and moods that provoke you to drink more, then you have made a start towards being moderate.

If you are a woman of reproductive age, you may notice that the menstrual cycle has something to do with your drinking pattern. Some surveys show that menstrual tension is related to greater recourse to alcohol in an attempt to relax.

■ Take concrete steps to resolve problems or conflicts. Stress leads to trying a drink as an antidote, but the real solution lies in tackling your particular problem. Escape via the bottle only causes more stress.

■ Try non-alcoholic or low alcohol beers and drinks. Take advantage of the increasing number of products now available that offer an enjoyable alternative to alcohol.

■ Pace your enjoyment of a drink. If you are adventurous, you could stock your refrigerator with the more unusual beverages, like guava fruit juice, or low alcohol cocktails. Then, at the end of a hard day, take your time sipping your drink. This is decompression time and after the first 20 minutes or so you may find you don't need the beer or the spirits in the same quantity after all.

■ Find alternative ways to dissipate stress. Swimming or gardening, listening to music or meditation; there are many healthy ways of de-stressing your life.

Should you find that you do not have the courage to kick the drinking habit on your own, then do not feel diffident about contacting Alcoholics Anonymous (See Reference List). They have a support network that makes it easier and possible for you to regain control of your life.

Substance Abuse

You may have sought refuge in other forms of substance abuse. This may be tranquillisers, sedatives or amphetamines. All are part of a situation which shows that one has inadequate resources for coping with stress.

The euphoric high created by narcotic drugs can never help you to cope with life. You may have started on the cocaine or marijuana road to escape from tedium or stress. You may end up as stress personified: nervous, angry, anxious, depressed, paranoid.

You will need professional counselling help.

COFFEE

Coffee owes its powers to a chemical compound better known as caffeine. Many people believe that a cup of coffee will give them the extra spurt of energy to tackle some forbidding task. Yet research has shown that the caffeine can build up layers of anxiety in some people. This 'background' anxiety builds up slowly so people do not always associate the coffee with the anxiety. The research also showed that the effect was most evident in people who drank more than four cups of coffee a day.

Beverages with caffeine in them – coffee, tea or a fizzy cola – may create stress but they can also raise blood pressure. One survey showed that if you were studying for your exams and consuming coffee or any other drink containing caffeine, then your blood pressure would be higher than if you were engaged in either of these individually. Secondly, the effect of caffeine lingers, raising average blood pressure for over two hours. If you are not so young, then your blood vessels are less elastic and the raised blood pressure could put extra strain on the blood vessels.

154

There is no need to feel that you will be deprived of your favourite hot drink. Decaffeinated coffee is now readily available in a number of brand names and the taste has been getting better all the time. So switch to a coffee without caffeine. Try a herbal tea. There are so many varieties to choose from that your finicky palate will surely find something acceptable.

COMPULSIVE SHOPPING

You have an argument with your teenage son/boss/spouse/partner. The next thing, you have compensated yourself for feeling low by splurging on a new pair of designer shoes/jacket or expensive sound system. It is quite normal (and human) for one to do this occasionally. One could call it impulse buying.

There are others, however, who are addicted to the 'high' of spending money recklessly, like the gambler at the race course. Compulsive shopping, like gambling, can lead to bankruptcy, embezzlement, selling the house, not to mention the havoc it causes in relationships.

Because of the availability of 'easy' or plastic money people can be tempted to spend without thinking of the consequences. But this is not the true cause of 'spendaholic' behaviour. Like compulsive eating, compulsive shopping can often be a self-destructive response to handling stress. Very often it is a response to rejection: if you went for a job interview or auditioned for a role and didn't get it, you may well go out and console yourself. But if you do this every time you face a test, you need to think about helping yourself in some other way.

You may not regard yourelf as a big spender, but may have had suspicions that you are one. Use the quiz to assess yourself. Do you:

1. Have trouble leaving a shop without buying something?

2. Buy things you don't need or want, but, because they are in a sale, they seem attractive to you?

3. Buy things on credit that you would not buy if you were paying cash?

4. Insist on paying the restaurant bill – then collect the cash from others at the table and pay by credit card?

5. Often divert money already allocated to important commitments towards your own splurges?

6. Always have to use a credit card to pay for emergencies – takeaway meals for unexpected guests or car repairs while travelling?

7. Always only pay the minimum balance on your accounts each month?

8. Attempt generally to beat your cheques to the bank?

9. Believe that having more money would solve most of your problems?

10. Feel preoccupied by thoughts of money, or uncomfortable at the thought of life without credit cards?

11. Feel obsessed by thoughts of spending any money that might be left over from your pay packet?

12. Feel defensive about your financial situation or debts that you might owe to family and friends? Do you, for example, hide new purchases from your partner?

If you answered 'yes' to five or more of these questions you may be a compulsive spender.

(Adapted with permission from SpenderMenders, Box 15000–156, San Francisco, CA94115)

Beating the Urge to Splurge
You will surely feel the need to tidy up your spending life. The first thing to do is to recognize that you deal with stress by spending money. The second is to attempt to deal with the

156

cause of the stress, rather than trying to offset it. If it is related to your work, use the advice on Executive Stress and On-the-Job Stress (see Index) to make a start. If it is your personal life, make a start on that front first.

Life being what it is, you cannot possibly practise abstinence from shopping. But you can take some steps towards protecting yourself from chronic spending splurges.

■ Cut up your credit cards. This is a major step and demands courage. If you do this, make sure that you have made alternative arrangements to have cash ready for essential expenditure and no more.

■ Avoid shopping when you are feeling lonely or depressed.

■ Don't use shopping as a recreation. Window shopping in the lunch hour is fine, but not for the compulsive shopper. Do something else – take a walk, read or write letters.

■ Always shop with a list, and a limit. Set yourself a defined objective and budget, and stick to it.

■ Allow yourself a 'cooling-off' period. Put the enticing dress back on the rail and wait for a day or two. If you really want to buy it, go back later.

■ Set some overall financial goal to attain. It may be saving for a holiday, or a new home. These are worthwhile goals and will put your compulsive urges in perspective.

If you have a set of good friends you can trust, talk to one of them about what is worrying you and what triggers off the urge to spend. You may well find a balanced view emerges and that they can help you gain confidence to withstand the temptation.

NERVOUS HABITS

Our body language reveals a great deal about us, but certain physical movements and behaviour can actually be the result of stress. The most common is nail-biting. Most of us know some unconfident and nervous person whose nails have been bitten and nibbled away almost to the cuticle. They do this as an automatic response to some situation they feel thay cannot cope with. Facial tics are another such habit, as is twisting a lock of hair round one's finger or pulling on a beard.

There is a way to break out of such responses. The first stage is to analyse when you start to do these things. The second is to develop a *competing* reaction. The third is to think about the stressful situation that makes you automatically put your hand to your lips.

Take nail-biting. Put a small piece of card in your briefcase or handbag. Each time you catch yourself chewing a nail make a slash in it. That will give you a tally. Or keep a litle notebook and make a note. This may show the day and the circum-stancesthat caused you to attack your nail. Did your boss shout at you? Was it just before your driving lesson? Or was it the pure boredom of waiting in the supermarket queue?

When you have formed a picture of nail-biting moments you can start to take action. The *competing* reaction involves placing your hands in a situation where you cannot bite your nails. Clutch a book, telephone, clench your fist, anything but leaving it free for nail-biting. Do this immediately after you have been biting your nails or as soon as you realize you are in the 'danger zone' that precedes nail-biting. If you deliberately practice your habit in front of your mirror you might detect little movements that signal an attack – rubbing your fingers or a movement of the hand up to the face. So when you next feel these coming on, go into *competing* reaction mode!

Carry an emery board to smooth your nails. Take pride in your hands and wear nail polish, rings or bangles – most nail-biters shy away from jewellery on the hand.

Finally, see if you can use some relaxing and affirmative

techniques to tackle the cause of your stress. (See Index, relaxation, assertiveness)

Tearing your Hair?

There are many nervous habits that people employ to relieve tension like foot tapping or finger drumming. Instead of these agitated movements calm yourself by steadying the foot or hand against some object – the rung of the chair or a table top or book. This creates the competing reaction.

The facial tic (including eye or shoulder twitches) can also be modified or changed. Occasionally there may be a neurological cause for these 'repetitive nonfunctional muscle contractions', but more often than not they are just a reaction to stress. Keep a diary and if the tics occur even when you are not under stress, you need to see a doctor. If not, use the competing reaction method.

For a muscle-contracting tic use the muscles which are developed in isometric exercises. If the tic involves raising one shoulder then start a strong two-minute tensing of the muscles that pull the shoulder down.

If you are a hair-puller use the tally system. Take up the hand-clenching method. If you have not been able to resist the urge, carry a comb and use this to calm yourself. After that repeat the hand-clenching for three minutes.

OVEREATING

Do you turn to chocolates when harried and upset? Do you stop after a nibble or two or just carry on guzzling? If the latter is true you are not the only one who associates food with comfort and solace.

One theory, based on animal experiments, has shown that eating sweets prompts the body to secrete endomorphins, natural opiate-like compounds in the brain, that dull pain. They therefore have the potential to act as a buffer to stress. Another theory suggests that high carbohydrate foods increase the production and release of serotonin, a nerve messenger that eases anxiety and tension.

Whatever the reason, 'eating away your troubles' is probably not as bad as drowning your sorrows or smoking away your problems. Nevertheless it is an unhealthy habit and leads to unwanted pounds and the attendant stress of trying to lose them. Secondly many of the foods that people favour in times of tension tend to be high in fat and sugar; that is unhealthy too.

What's Eating You?

If you are concerned about your relationship between food and stress, you could keep a diary of what prompted you to eat and what you chose. The diet diary may reveal that nothing has changed – your boss is still a fool, your car still needs repairs, or your budget still needs sorting out. It might induce you to think of means of remedying the situation rather than seeking recourse to food.

To take preventive action keep these basic principles in mind:

■ Eat regular, nutritious meals. If you are dieting, continue to eat regularly otherwise you will set yourself up for stress-induced binges.

■ Distract yourself if you feel the urge to eat coming on. Take a walk, listen to music, read, and then ask yourself, 'Do I still feel like eating?'.

■ Expect relapses. We are surrounded by opportunities to indulge ourselves so it would be naive to expect total success. And don't let yourself feel guilty.

There is no blame attached to relying on food for help in times of stress. And there is some truth in the theory of oral gratification – the chewing and sucking throwback from

160

infancy. But chewing, whether it is gum or a jelly baby is not the ideal solution.

However if you feel this offers an option, keep carrot and celery sticks handy, dried apricots or other healthy alternatives to chocolates.

SMOKING

Nicotine is a mood-altering substance. It may help you cope with loneliness, anxiety, stress. *And* it improves concentration, which is why so many people in high-pressure jobs — doctors, air traffic controllers, business executives and nurses – smoke. Whenever you face tasks that are too demanding nicotine, and other chemicals in cigarette smoke can reduce fatigue and transform your mood.

However, nicotine is a drug and it is addictive. This instant stress relief has enormous disadvantages. There is now no doubt that tobacco causes lung cancer and is related to the development of heart disease. Smoking and stress, hand-in-hand, raise blood pressure more than either smoking or stress on their own. It has other nasty effects. A recent report from Action on Smoking and Health (ASH) says that cigarette smoking affects the face and causes premature ageing of the skin.

Cigarettes, like alcohol, are a legal product. They are available easily and says, one expert, can be used to dose yourself precisely. You can take a tiny puff or inhale deeply, smoke frequently or occasionally, buy a strong or a mild pack. Unlike cocaine or other drugs, nicotine doesa not peoduce a tremendous rush of feeling and then a crash.

That is one reason why the habit is so difficult to break. The other is that one can smoke while engaged in any number of activities – working at your desk, driving in the car or watching televsion. These are almost conditioned responses – if you are having a drink the instinct is to associate this with a cigarette as well.

You could talk to your doctor about help with giving up the habit, whether it is joining a programme to give up smoking or taking nicotine-flavoured chewing gum. Action on Smoking and Health (See Reference List) will also be able to give you useful information. Reducing the chances for the stress-related reaction that causes you to reach for the cigarette is also a good place to start.

Here are some tips that may be helpful when faced by the urge to smoke:

■ Sit it out. If you are under pressure and dying for a cigarette, understand that fatigue and stress come and go. So will the urge to smoke, so try to wait and not reach for the packet.

■ Talk yourself out of it. Instead of thinking, 'I can't get through this job without a smoke', say to yourself, 'Wait a minute. Slow down. I *can* survive without a cigarette'.

■ Use your imagination. When you are dying to smoke distract attention away from the thought by imagining a pleasurable situation. It could be swimming in warm, tropical waters, or skiing on snowy slopes. You could make a mental list of the stressful situations that cause you to smoke. When you encounter one of these, activate your happy thought and you will reduce your risk of lighting up.

■ Practise deep breathing. This relates to the way you inhale cigarette smoke. While watching televsion you might take light puffs – your mind is occupied with entertainment. At the office with a mountain of work, you will probably attack a difficult project with the cigarette for support, and inhale deeply to get the utmost benefit from the nicotine. So turn the deep breathing to your advantage without the cigarette. Stand up, bend forward from the waist and breathe deeply for 15 to 30 seconds, or however long it takes to fully expel the air from your lungs. You will feel a sense of relaxation without the cigarette.

■ Take a break. If the task in hand is complex and seems unmanageable, take a brisk walk for the amount of time it would take you to smoke a cigarette. Get yourself a drink of water, or chat to someone briefly. Change the predictable pattern of reaching for the packet.

■ Try to tackle the stress you may be under. This may be realistic setting of goals, or good time management. Both may help to prevent the overload of stress that leads to the cigarette.

When you are free of the habit (having used whichever strategy was best for you) accept the fact that you will continue to crave for cigarettes for some months. The desire may be intense and you may encounter everyday, ordinary situations (like talking on the phone) which will trigger the need for the cigarette. If you last the first six months, you might be out of the woods. Once you have given up smoking it is not nicotine that keeps you hooked. It is the moods, circumstances and events that trigger the urge to smoke. So remain vigilant and resist the temptation.

6

COPING TECHNIQUES THAT WORK

Assertiveness Training ■ *Autogenic Training*

Baths ■ *Biofeedback* ■ *Cognitive Therapy*

Deep Breathing ■ *Delegating*

Doodles and Diaries ■ *Exercise*

Time Management ■ *Holidays* ■ *Walking*

Flotation Tanks ■ *Friends and Family*

Hobbies and Play ■ *Household Appliances*

Imagery ■ *Laughter* ■ *Love and Romance*

Massage ■ *Music* ■ *Nature*

Nutrition ■ *Pets* ■ *Positive Thinking*

Prayer and Religion ■ *Rest Breaks*

Self-Help Groups ■ *Sex* ■ *Sleep*

ASSERTIVENESS TRAINING

You buy a toaster which fails to toast. You do one of three things.

1. You stay at home and fume about the inferior quality of modern appliances.

2. You storm back to the shops, demand to see the manager, scream and yell about how you're tired of getting ripped off. You insist on getting your money back and you march out of the shop.

3. You return to the shop, calmly ask to speak with the manager and, in a very earnest, straightforward manner, explain that your toaster is not working satisfactorily and that you would either like it replaced or your money back

Now which of these situations produces the most stress?

If you're the stay-at-home-and-fume type, you're probably too passive for your own good. If you're number **2**, you may be too aggressive for your own good. Option **3**, of course, is to be assertive, to know your rights and to respect the rights of others, and to have polished skills in effectively communicating your message without hostility.

Let's look at another situation. You're at a party where you know very few people. You want to mingle so what do you do?

1. You hang around on the fringes of other people's conversations, waiting for them to include you.

2. You burst into a group and dominate the conversation. One by one the members wander away, and when each one does, you shout, 'You're missing a golden opportunity!'

3. You approach a group with an effective opening line, such as 'Are you enjoying the party', or 'How do you know the host?'

166

Again, which solution appears least stressful?

Assertive behaviour wins hands down over the passive or aggressive solution in reducing stress. But too many of us have been programmed to respond badly. Girls are generally reared to be too passive. Boys are sometimes treated as if aggression is a birthright. On top of that, we have not grown up in general to learn from people who exhibit calm, clear, assertive behaviour.

Without the benefit of either upbringing or role models, the only way to learn this behaviour may be assertiveness training. Through this you can unlearn anxiety-response habits. It does not take long. It not only makes you more effective in all your relationships with other people, but you become more open, understand the consequences of your actions and life becomes less stressful. There are many courses available now, and an excellent Channel 4 television series introduced by Manuel (of *Fawlty Towers*) and John Cleese. Almost everyone can gain from the courses but they are a must for people who generally fear what others think of them, are dissatisfied with social relationships, or frequently experience bouts of depression, frustration, anger, helplessness and feeling pushed around by others. Look at the leaflets about such courses and see whether you prefer group or individual training.

You can also see how you handle situations at work. Responding to pressures with tears or with anger are indicators that you need to seek a new approach. Just remember, you are not giving up your right to say or feel something – you are altering the way that you do it.

On the active side, as opposed to holding back your aggression, you need to set yourself some small tasks, such as striking up conversations with a fellow passenger on the bus or in a queue in the shops. You'll be amazed at how nice people can be. You can also decide that sometimes you are going to say no. And that can be part of your body language, not just verbalization. The obvious example is your eyes concentrating on the smoke from someone else's cigarette in a restaurant. If they do not respond by putting it out, politely ask them if they would not mind smoking while you are eating. Try it out while watching yourself in the mirror. And do not forget to evaluate the assertiveness training itself – maybe the instructor is too lax or too aggressive.

AUTOGENIC TRAINING

Imagine being able simply to tell your body to relax and having it respond! That's the aim of autogenic training, a form of self-hypnosis that is amongst the best and most complete reducers of stress. The technique was developed by Doctors Johannes Schultz and Wolfgang Luthe at the start of the century and is a combination of their medical research and yoga. The result is a series of self-instructions that can help the body rid itself of ailments such as high blood pressure, headaches, chronic pain, allergies, ulcers and general anxiety. It can also induce deep relaxation.

You tell yourself what you want (My heartbeat is calm and regular) and you produce the desired physical results. As you practise the training on a regular basis, you'll discover it becomes easier to instruct your body to reply. Part of what's happening is that you relax to a point where your body's self-regulating systems take over. The relaxation brings about the physical change. It may take weeks or longer to use autogenic training to bring about a physiological result such as increased thyroid production. If you practise the relaxation techniques we have discussed earlier you can get satisfactory results in the first session.

How to Do It

You should carry out your relaxation in a quiet room, the lights down low and wearing loose clothing. You should sit in an armchair that supports your head, back and extremities comfortably. You can use a bean bag, or lie down with your head supported by a cushion or pillow, feet slightly apart and arms at your side but not touching your body. You should be free of tension.

168

The instructions outlined by Dr Shaffer in his book, *Life atfer Stress* , are as follows. Close your eyes, breathe deeply and evenly and as you exhale say these 'cues' aloud to yourself:

1. 'My hands and arms are heavy and warm' (5 times)

2. 'My feet and legs are heavy and warm' (5 times)

3. 'My abdomen is warm and comfortable' (5 times). (Omit this step if you have ulcers).

4. 'My breathing is deep and even' (10 times).

5. 'My heartbeat is slightly calm and regular' (10 times). (Use of the word *slightly* in this step can help prevent the reaction of a rapid, irregular heartbeat which some people experience when that word is omitted).

6. 'My forehead is cool' (5 times).

7. 'When I open my eyes, I will remain relaxed and refreshed' (3 times).

Perform the following sequence of body movements:

1. Move your hands and arms about.

2. Move your feet and legs about.

3. Rotate your head.

4. Open your eyes and sit up.

All of this should be done with an attitude of passive concentration. Observe what's happening to your body, but don't consciously try to analyse it. By all means don't criticize yourself for having distracting thoughts. If your mind wanders, simply bring it back to your instructions as soon as possible.

Doctor Shaffer suggests two-minute autogenic training sessions ten times a day. 'If you spend ten little times a day bringing your tension level down, it's unlikely to get up that high.'

Unexpected Results

You may experience 'autogenic discharges'. These can be tingling or other body sensations, involuntary movements, pain or even a desire to cry. These feelings may be pleasant or unpleasant, but they will pass as you progress. Just tell yourself this is normal, as it is, because the brain is dumping your tensions through your motor system.

Beware of lying back and, instead of feeling relaxed, lapsing into a panic of anxiety. 'That happens with people who need tension as a defence,' Dr Shaffer says. 'They're getting rid of their tension and up comes anxiety. Things they've not paid attention to are coming up to the surface.' He suggests letting it pass and continuing with the autogenic formula. If the anxiety continues he suggests you talk to a doctor or expert.

In any case, because autogenic training produces physiological changes, it's not something to take lightly. If you have high or low blood pressure, diabetes, hypoglycaemia or a heart condition, you should consult your doctor beforehand. People with severe mental or emotional disorders are discouraged from trying autogenic training. If you find yourself feeling restless during or after autogenic sessions – or if you suffer disquieting side effects – practise it only under the supervision of a professional autogenic training instructor.

Bidding Migraines Adieu

Some professional therapists hook people up to biofeedbackmachines to monitor the physiological changes that occur during autogenic changes. A number of US clinics believe the combination of the two can be a powerful tool to get rid of migraines, although this view is not so common in countries such as the UK. The issue for migraine suffers, of course, is not why it works but if it works for them. (See Reference List)

The aim is to reduce overdilation of the arteries by neurochemicals as spelt our earlier in the section on headaches and migraines. (See Index, headaches)

Part of the technique, when signs such as blurred vision show that a migraine is imminent, is to visualize warming the hands – burying them in warm sand for example. Psychology Professor Dr Jack Hartje says that those who get no warning of an attack are taught to keep their hands warm all the time. One practical method is a daily session of autogenic training until the hand-warming becomes second nature.

BATHS

New Yorker Dana Horwitz would win a gold medal if there was an event at the Olympics for taking baths. She has spent years perfecting her technique. As well as a fixed number of times for taking a bath she takes every opportunity to fit in an extra one, such as when she wakes up early. She says that she finds 10 or 15 minutes soaking in the bath wakes her up.

Her last 'p.m.' bath at night prepares her for sleep. 'How can people say they relax in the shower? Standing on one's feet can't be relaxing when you could be lying down.'

In between the occasional morning splash and evening bath, she soaks before lunch appointments, important meetings with friends, or to get away from her two children teasing each other. Experts agree with her that taking a bath is a stress-management technique similar to meditation or relaxation.

Not Too Warm, Not Too Cold...

A word of warning – avoid hot baths if you are pregnant, have high blood pressure, nerve impairment or diabetes.

Despite much experience since the day we were first bathed as a baby, there is a routine to follow. So grab a thermometer and keep reading. The water should be the same temperature as your skin, between 85F and 93F, depending where on the skin you measure it. So you can use around 90F and 95F. Colder water will be unpleasant and stimulate, not relax tense muscles. Too hot and you will begin to perspire. Keep the

171

temperature right by allowing hot water to drip from the tap. Stay soaking for 20 to 30 minutes, and use a foam pillow to rest your head. If you are relaxing before going to bed, then when it is time to get out, towel off, get your pyjamas on straightaway and march straight to bed — no reading, no television — just close your eyes and drift off.

The Scandinavians have developed Saunas to a fine art and there is extensive literature on the subject on how hot, how long and when. The procedure is to have high, dry heat alternating with a cold shower. Steam baths which work on you through wet heat are popular with others, as are jacuzzis and hot tubs. These all tend to stimulate the body rather than relax it, but for those using them they also produce feelings of relaxation and wellbeing. The same precautions for people with a health problem should be borne in mind as for hot baths.

BIOFEEDBACK

Biofeedback machines work by measuring perspiration or the amount of electrical activity on the skin. If you remember that it is only a tool that indicates the level of your heart activity, breath rate etc., then you will have begun to understand its function. The important element is how you control these functions — the machine helps you to assess what control you have of them. By being aware of stress in this way you can reduce it. You become the expert on yourself.

The availability of biofeedback units, handheld ones and desk models is far more extensive in North America than Europe. In the US the cost ranges from $30 to $100 or more. If you have your own computer at home there is also an American software called Calmpute which does the same job. Another US gadget called Calmtone lets you connect a biofeedback unit to your stereo and the music goes louder or softer in synchronization with your relaxation. Instead of visual signals some other machines let you hear the changes through headphones with slower and faster clicks.

Geoffrey Wendell of Audio Limited which supplies various biofeedback systems in the UK (See Reference List) says he prefers equipment which gives specific readings at the start and finish of monitoring. This gives you fixed values which you can note and compare from day to day whereas the audio systems give no fixed point for comparison. His background is in electronics and he became interested in this field through the work of Maxwell Cade. Cade, who is now dead, and his surviving wife Isabel Cade, ran the school of Contemporary Studies, which over the years examined a number of relaxation techniques involving some 5,000 students in toto. You can find contact points for further information about this and other techniques, such as the Alexander Method, through the Institute of Complementary Medicine. (See Reference List)

COGNITIVE THERAPY – SELF-TALK

You're standing in a crowded lift. Someone is standing on the back of your shoes. As you turn around to give them a piece of your mind you suddenly see that it is a little old lady on crutches. Immediately your anger subsides. You *thought* the person was intentionally annoying you and the distorted picture you built up in your mind produced a negative feeling. That is what cognitive therapy is all about – thoughts determine feelings and *negative* thoughts almost always engender gross distortions. By recognizing distorted negative thoughts we can learn to change them. A good example is the fire-engine siren or bell – you should not be trapped into thinking that it is your own house that is on fire. Nor should you think that you are for the high jump if you are called in to see your supervisor at work, or that your teenage daughter or son are late home for no good reason. Always say to yourself that the supervisor is going to give you some new interesting work or compliment you, and that your apparently errant child has as good an excuse as the last time they were home late. The trick is to explain that it is better that they call to say they would be late so that you can go to bed without having to worry.

173

Straightening out the Distortions

When your mood changes, and you find you are anxious or angry then do an instant replay. Examine your thinking and see if you can identify some of these reactions:

■ All-or-nothing: If you have a knock with the car you blame yourself as totally incompetent. If you lose your job you are the world's worst failure. It is not true – nothing is so black and white.

■ Don't jump to conclusions: The rest of the day is not going to be a disaster because the car would not start first thing.

■ Don't mind read: People may always look bad tempered, but perhaps they were born that way.

■ 'Well-Chaosed': Don't turn the slightest thing into a disaster. Even if you forgot to post the monthly hire-purchase payment, tomorrow will still come. Just ring up to say you missed the post and it is on the way.

■ Mental filtering: Don't block out the good and only let the negative come through. Your son forgot your birthday (for the first time) and instead of remembering his good qualities you only think he is a louse.

■ 'Over-moaning': The type of person who not only believes they will never be happy but also that everything should be fair, needs to make a list of what real events are like. Use the television news to see how many people never get their wish. This will help you to understand setbacks and enjoy your successes.

■ In an acute situation, such as pre-interview butterflies, scribble on the edge of a newspaper:
   Your situation: My friend hasn't called to wish me luck.'
   Your feeling: Sadness.

What you're telling yourself at the time: He only thinks of himself.

In a few moments you will see that your apprehension not only has no basis in reality (he probably told you he was not going to be near a phone) but also will not affect your interview.

Most of our difficulties in this area are with acquaintances and relatives. While you should always leave the door open to friendship, the fact is that many of us have different chemistries and if there is no clear problem between you to sort out, then accept the reality. It will at least bring some respect. No one likes Aunt Hilary in *Neighbours* but they do respect her.

More important for yourself is the disadvantage of continuing to say something, whether it is true or false. So always say the positive thing – like Aunt Hilary!

DEEP BREATHING

When you compare the smooth breathing of a newborn baby and a middle-aged adult you quickly realize that one of them has forgotten how to breathe. Stress takes a long-term toll on your breathing. It becomes short and shallow while it should in fact extend all the way down to your abdomen. Stress also makes you pant, or hold your breath and that compounds the problem, and of course you get less oxygen and more carbon dioxide.

Dr Rushkin of the Kripalu Center for Yoga and Health offers the following method on how to breathe:

1. Sit, relaxed, but with spine straight and shoulders back (but down and loose) to allow your lungs to expand. Rest your hands on the arms of the chair or in your lap. Put your feet on the floor.

2. Breathe in slowly through your nose as you expand your abdomen and, as you inhale, you're slowly inflating it, causing

175

COPING TECHNIQUES THAT WORK

the abdominal area to to swell.

3. Breathe out slowly through your nose. Pull your abdominal muscles in as you press all the air out of your lungs.

4. Continue breathing in and out as your abdomen rises and falls. Establish a natural rhythm. To feel this, place your hands on your abdomen just above the navel with fingertips pointing towards each other and just touching. If you're breathing correctly, your hands will rise with your abdomen as you inhale, and your fingertips will separate. As you exhale they will touch again.

The cleansing breath releases tension quickly:

1. Inhale through your nose.

2. Exhale through your puckered mouth, as if you were blowing out a candle.

3. Repeat steps 1 and 2 three times.

4. Issue a few sighs. Inhale deeply, then sigh. Again. Again. With each sigh, drop your chin to your chest and droop your shoulders. Think of yourself as a tyre deflating. Think of the tension you are releasing.

The stress-discharging breath:

Allow more time to do this exercise. It's perfect for after work.

1. Make sure you will not be disturbed.

2. Get into a comfortable position, lying down or sitting in a favourite chair. Loosen any constricting clothing.

3. Start relaxing with several abdominal breaths; breath in to the count of four, then breathe out to the count of eight.

4. Take a deep breath through your nose and hold it. Tense your feet as long as you can. (Warning: if you have a history of heart disease, high blood pressure or stroke, consult your doctor about this technique. He or she may suggest a modified version, with little or no breath-holding).

5. Relax your feet as you exhale with a sigh through your mouth.

6. Take a few abdominal breaths with each count, as in step **3**.

7. Breathe in deeply through your nose. Hold it. Tense your calves.

8. Relax your calves as you breathe out with a strong exhalation.

9. Repeat the sequence for each area of the body, working from the extremities to the centre: feet, calves, thighs, bottom, abdomen. Next, the upper body: fingers, forearms, upper arms, shoulders. (Hunch your shoulders up to your ears). Don't forget your face. It may hold much tension. Work it in three stages: pull your jaw back so your mouth looks funny; scrunch up your nose; furrow on your brow.

10. Take a few minutes to relax and let go.

The waiting (in a queue) peacefully breath. Banks and post offices should print copies of this exercise on index cards and distribute them to customers.

It works!

1. Do the slow, deep, abdominal breath with long, relaxed exhalation. Feel impatience drifting away. (In a traffic jam, don't breathe too deeply).

2. Continue the abdominal breath. As you relax, realize that impatience will not get you to the front of the queue any faster — it only makes the time longer.

3. See those around you as fellow human beings also waiting and working to the best of their ability.

4. Imagine how pleasurable it would be if everyone around you was also relaxed and trying new ways to be patient and efficient.

DELEGATING

Carol hates doing the shopping but her family has to eat and she has had to drag herself to the supermarket once a week and resented pushing a trolley up and down the aisles. Her 12–year-old daughter, Ann, loves to shop, and not only enjoys the atmosphere of the supermarket but avidly cuts out all the offers for discounts. So Carol has done them both a favour by delegating the shopping to Ann who thrives on it while mother avoids the stress.

Why a Woman's Work is Never Done

Whether you are managing a household of two, a small business or a major division of a multinational, delegating not only increases your control but takes a load of stress off your shoulders. Unfortunately, too few of use our workplace delegating skills in the home, and women have the most to gain from this because the house is usually a second job, with the woman putting in five to eight hours a day compared to the man's one or two hours.

How to Delegate Without Distress

■ Decide which jobs you can unload. Make a list of all the routine jobs around the house, starting with the dog or locking the door at night, and decide what you can delegate. Crucial decisions should be kept for you. One woman delegated the job of keeping track of birthdays, and buying and sending the cards, to her teenage son.

■ Give clear, complete instructions, as good as a supermarket shopping list. The more precise you are the more satisfaction you and they will get at a job well done. And don't forget to set a *deadline* .

■ Don't be a dictator. A child can be told to clean their room once a week without the day and hour being laid down – unless you need to get them used to the idea!

■ Offer encouragement, not ridicule. Realize that it is not true that no one can do the job as well as you. It is not wise to criticize people the first time they do a job so they do not want to help again. The 'delegator' then complains that they do not get enough help. Dr Ann Crouter, from Pennsylvania University, says that you must accept that people will make some mistakes; encourage, not criticize, and they'll get it right next time. She explains that since her husband shops and cooks, she praises his cooking 'as graciously as she can'. Praise a child in the same way, she says.

■ Make work fun – children can become great cooks when they are preparing something they like.

■ Rotate unpopular jobs.

■ Don't feel guilty. Not only only is delegating good for you, it is good for others' self-reliance. There is nothing worse than seeing children or elderly widows or widowers, who find themselves on their own and incapable, because someone else had always kept them out of household chores. While a man needs to know how to cook or wash, so a woman should also know how to cope with those minor car problems which are always assumed must be left to the male. So let the whole family learn surival skills through delegation.

DOODLES AND DIARIES

Dr Janie Rhyne, a psychologist at the University of Iowa School of Social Work, runs workshops to show people how to use doodle diaries to relieve their stress. Her students keep their doodles in a notebook, each doodle accompanied by a few words about what they are feeling at the time – annoyance, anger, happiness etc. She says that the doodles are visual expressions of what people experience internally and so it helps bring feelings out into the open.

Diaries Are Good Therapy

A written diary works on the same principle. It is particularly helpful to deal with very personal problems about which you cannot talk to anyone else. It also forces you to slow down, organize your thoughts and give the problem a concrete structure. Men probably benefit more than women because they have difficulty opening up to others. Experts also suggest that it helps bring deep-rooted, long-past problems to the surface, such as the trauma of a earlier divorce.

A regular diary writer will also cope better with problems when they occur. A control study of students showed that those who wrote about problems for 20 minutes a day for four days had an increased level of white cell activity which increases resistance to infection through the immune system. The effect lasted for six weeks, according to the blood test results. Those who had written about things they had avoided in the past gained the most benefit. A diary also helps to pinpoint links between stress and ailments such as headaches.

How to Use Your Pocket Therapist

Here are some guidelines on running a diary:

1. Begin at the beginning by writing down the 'stepping stones' of your life and how you got to where you are today.

2. Write when you feel the need, like taking a headache

tablet, rather than on a fixed schedule.

3. Put yourself in the right frame of mind by meditating or doing a relaxation exercise before you start to write.

4. Try to put down your deepest thoughts and feelings.

5. Don't just write that you feel miserable or happy but *why*.

6. If there is someone you want to talk to about something but feel you cannot, then make up an imaginary dialogue on paper.

7. The diary is for you and it will not be honest unless you keep it totally anonymous so no one else can make it out. (See 'Keeping a Stress Diary' in the Appendix)

EXERCISE

As you move through your day there will be more than one opportunity to get angry, perhaps in traffic, at an unexpected bill or someone who gets you going. If your anger subsides as quickly as it arose then you are probably no worse for the event. If not, part of your body is going to pump out a potentially toxic substance called noradrenalin, which is triggered with adrenalin when your body senses trouble. Dr Redford B. Williams, Professor of Psychiatry at Duke University, says that this noradrenalin effect can easily be dealt with, not only by venting your feelings, but by exercising to burn it off. Exercise, some experts say, floods the body with natural painkillers called endorphins and these relieve tension either directly, or by slowing down your breathing. There are suggestions from studies that reading and running can both produce the effect of taking your mind off a problem and so relieve stress. Swimmers also say they feel in a much better mood after a session in the pool, with more patience, control of their surroundings and a capacity for getting on with things.

Fit People Handle Stress Better

There are other studies which also show that people who keep
fit, whatever their age and however they do it, have less
depression and fewer physical ailments and do not suffer as
much from "bad experiences' as the unfit. We all remember
the relief and release of the school break after a morning of
lessons and the same should be built into your adult day –
many people now go jogging during their lunch break to
achieve this effect.

The Exercise Prescription

Researchers say that the most effective stress-reducing
exercises are continuous activities such as aerobics, running,
walking, swimming and cross-country skiing. 'Stop and go'
sports are not as good but still worthwhile if you enjoy them.
The table below is drawn up by Dr Landers of Arizona State
University who rated them for their approximate potential
for reducing tension.

Activity	Rating when performed at 70% higher of maximum heart rate*	Rating when performed at 30–40% of max heart rate+
Aerobics	5	2
Badminton (stop/go)	3	1
Basketball (stop/go)	3	1
10–pin bowling	1	1
Calisthenics	4	2
Canoeing	2	1
Circuit-training	5	3
X-country skiing	5	3
Cycling	5	3
Dancing	2	1
Frisbee	2	1
Golf (foursome, pulling clubs)	2	1
Hiking	3	2

Activity	Rating when performed at 70% higher of maximum heart rate*	Rating when performed at 30–40% of max heart rate+
Hiking (with 10lb backpack)	4	3
Ice skating	3	2
Martial arts	3	1
Racquetball, squash, handball	3	1
Roller-skating	3	1
Skipping	4	2
Rowing	5	3
Running	5	3
Softball	3	1
Swimming (crawl)	5	3
Table tennis	3	1
Tennis (singles)	3	1
Tennis (doubles)	2.5	1
Volleyball	3	1
Water skiing	3	1
Windsurfing	2	1
Yoga	4	3

* By well-conditioned individuals
+ By less conditioned individuals

To get the optimum Relaxation Response from exercise, you should work out a minimum of three times a week for at least 20 minutes, at a moderate or vigorous level i.e. 70 to 80 per cent of your maximum heart rate (this should be roughly 220, minus your age). Check with your doctor if you are in doubt about how much to do.

Dr Robert Brown, of the University of Virginia, says that a healthy 20–year-old should begin to feel the effects of an exercise programme a few days after starting it. People aged 40 or more may need a month or more to feel the full effects.

T'ai Chi is one of many approaches to exercise which we have learnt from the East and which you can do at any age. The essence of it is the maintenance of a particular posture through a series of slow, dancelike motions. These allow a free flow of energy through the body, producing a high degree of relaxation, strength and alertness. At its higher level it also combines meditation and martial arts. Because it improves your posture it also tones up the muscles to do what they should be doing.

TIME MANAGEMENT

Throughout the book we have stressed the importance of time and making sure you do things regularly. If you are short of time, or have too much, then you need to sort out a routine. Pencil and paper are easy to find but time-management diaries are also very cheap now.

Useful guidelines:

1. Make a personal inventory of how you spend your time over a few weeks, using 30–minute sections. That will show you what you are up to and where you can 'manage' your time better.

2. Draft out your goals and aims over the next six months and the next few years. You can fantasize about major and minor aims, whether in your career or DIY around the house. Put it up on the wall and see how you get on.

3. Draw up a daily agenda – expect to spend 15 minutes a day on it.

4. Set specific and realistic deadlines.

5. At the end of each week and each month set aside an hour (or less if needed) to see where you got to. It can be quite satisfying.

6. Eliminate your ten biggest time gobblers.

7. Learn to block out interruptions.

8. Be ready to say no if someone comes up a second time with a real time-waster.

9. See what you can delegate from your list.

10. Be prepared – setting the breakfast table at night, and making sure you are ready for the off the night before is just one example of saving time and stress.

HOLIDAYS

Holidays are essential. Yet many people fail to take them even when entitled to them. Cost should have nothing to do with it. If you turn them into a marathon of effort they are not holidays. If you have small children then you can go hiking and hostelling in inexpensive comfort. Don't necessarily stay at home – unless you are someone who spends your year travelling, in which case being at home may be a holiday in itself.

The time to get ready for a holiday is when the signs begin to pop up – irritable in the morning, feeling overwhelmed and jumpy. Even a weekend break can do wonders. Don't let your tension get too bad because it will take you so long to unwind that you will mess up your break.

Taking a break does not mean just lying on your back. You should ensure that your holiday includes things to do and they should be different from your work week. Just as important is not to overdo the activity side and leave no time for unwinding.

So:

1. Stop running – physically, mentally and emotionally.

2. Resolve any feelings of guilt about wasting time.

3. Learn to tolerate fantasy and play.

4. Savour the serenity of it.

185

In the general scheme of things holidays are elements in a preventive package and should not be a substitute for tackling underlying problems. That is what the rest of this book has been about.

WALKING

We have already said that walking is one of the best forms of exercise. Some American supermarkets are actually opening up early so that pensioners can pace themselves around the aisles and do their requisite number of miles each day in a safe and trouble-free environment. What is clear about walking is that once the habit is established many people feel that they cannot do without it and become addicted – a healthy addiction.

Walking increases the oxygen flow, strengthens your heart, loosens up your joints, works off extra weight, lowers your blood pressure and gears your body up to react to the fight-or-flight position when faced by stress. Certainly, walking off a problem is more likely to succeed than sitting or lying there brooding about it – it is a form of relieving 'mental indigestion'.

How Far, How Fast, How Long?

Start out by strolling at a slow, even pace. Try to keep walking for about 20 minutes. Over a week or two build up to about one to one and half miles, basically walking at about three to four miles an hour. Exercise about three times a week and if you have a friendly doctor check you heart rate before you start the first time so you can see what level you need to get you up to the desirable 70 to 80 per cent of your maximum heart rate. Warm up each time by starting slowly and then increasing the tempo and at the end of the walk slow down. Dr John Pleas from Nashville walks 97 miles a week and celebrates his birthdays with 24–hour walks. He recommends proper breathing where you exhale twice as long as you inhale in a rhythmic manner. Also keep your posture correct by looking ahead of yourself or focusing on a tree or telegraph pole.

Do's and Don'ts:
If a dog troubles you :

■ Ignore the dog.

■ Walk briskly and with confidence.

■ Stop and tell it firmly to go home.

■ Go with a friend the next time.

■ Find the owner and say you will call the police!

Don't:

■ Show fear.

■ Run from the dog.

■ Threaten it.

■ Throw anything at it.

■ Pet it.

■ Give up walking.

Do:

■ Check the weather forecast.

■ Let someone know where you're going and when you're back.

187

■ Wear light-coloured clothing and a reflecting band.

■ Wear comfortable shoes.

■ Carry some form of identification.

■ Carry change for the phone.

■ Walk facing the traffic on narrow roads.

■ Call the police if you think you're being followed.

In addition don't:

■ Have a drink before you leave if you have a weak bladder.

■ Continue walking if you become ill.

■ Take refuge under a tree if there is lightning.

■ Walk too quickly at night on bad surfaces.

■ Cross at a red light to maintain your momentum.

■ Give up walking.

You'll Never Walk Alone

There are hundreds of thousands of you out there walking and the number is growing everyday. You can join long-distance walking clubs when you get better and there are plenty of short-walk club meets in most cities with any kind of historical background though time spent in the pub at the end can be counterproductive!

Attitude adjustment

Even thinking of exercise causes some of us stress, particularly if it is one more job on top of daily demands. So if you do not have a motive such as the excitement of competition, then you must overcome inhibitions such as not showing your spindly legs in public and using that as an excuse to drop out.

So:

■ Pick an exercise you like.

■ Draw up and keep to an exercise schedule.

■ Don't take up a competitive exercise if it drives you to excess, and avoid competitive partners.

■ Choose more than one activity – variety is the spice of life.

■ Choose relaxing surroundings – parks rather than roads, and an area or sports centre you know so you feel comfortable there. Or plump for home with an exercise videotape.

■ Keep your exercise kit or swimming costume in your bag or car so it is always easy to hand.

■ Exercise to music you like particularly to relieve the monotony of repetitive excerises or 'long-distance' ones.

Any stress you incur by adding it to your daily routine will be far outweighed by the benefits.

FLOTATION TANKS

Flotation tanks, in their early days called 'sensory-deprivation tanks', are no longer coffins, dark as a cave and filled with salty water, in laboratory basements. Today's versions, which make you feel more relaxed than you have ever felt before after half

189

an hour floating, are larger and may have a control panel with an intercom, and allowing use of light and music to reduce the level of isolation.

The salty water allows effortless floating, and with all sound and light sealed out, the body's borders are blurred, gravity is removed and you can feel the tension flowing from your muscles. The proven stress-reducing effects are many.

Clearing Away Stress Biochemicals

Under stress, the body releases several biochemicals – blood cortisol, norepinephrine and epinephrine (adrenalin) – that can produce high blood pressure and muscular tension. Researchers believe that a certain time in the tank reduces these. Deprived of stimuli, the body seems to use its inner mechanism to return to an optimal, functioning level, with heart rate and blood pressure going down. Researchers also believe that capillaries restricted during stress become dilated and send a better flow of blood back to the extremities. Dr Roderick Borrie in New York says that floaters also cope better with stress afterwards for several days. His rheumatoid arthritis patients get pain relief for three to four days after two sessions a week. He also uses it as his consulting couch by talking to patients through an intercom. The St Elizabeth Hospital in Appleton, Wisconsin finds between 70 and 80 per cent improvement in the treatment of problems including anxiety, gastrointestinal ailments, chronic pain and headaches.

FRIENDS AND FAMILY

A high phone bill does not necessarily mean that you have verbal diarrhoea! It may be a good sign that you are using the phone as a personal defence strategy to reduce stress by talking to others. For example, it is a good sign if you ring your parents, sisters or brothers to enlist their support. The phone has become one of the most effective weapons modern society has to replace the personal links lost through the disappearance of village communities. The extensive use of the consulting couch in North America could well be a reflection of the fact that people may have lost the ability and ease to communicate and share problems with others that is common in areas of Europe such as Italy. To seek comfort and support it may be that a close friend or confidante can be as effective as your personal 'shrink'.

Medical evidence indicates that people who enjoy contact with and support from others, when faced with a crisis, tend to maintain a higher level of morale and also suffer fewer physical problems. One study confirmed this amongst a group of pregnant women under stress who, because of their support systems, had one third the complications of other pregnant women. This has something to say about the medicalization of birth in hospital with strangers in attendance, rather than the security of a home birth with a midwife, in touch from the early days of pregnancy through to the first few months of a baby's life.

Another study showed that people who lost their jobs and had no support system to turn to, suffered much more ill health than those who did and also had higher cholesterol levels.

For those lucky enough to have a large and closely-knit family there is no need to explain the advantages of always having someone there to help or sympathize. A family that is constantly at war within itself needs to learn how to praise itself and its members. Another factor, of course, is that sometimes a close friend may be easier to talk to about certain issues, particularly if they affect an individual's relationship with the family.

Family teamwork is one of the best ways of reducing the day-to-day stresses of life. If you do not have your 'own' family, then you need to set about creating one. Make a list of 20 people whom you know you can rely on, or whom you think might support you. If there are not 20 then find them. Other people on their own need this as much as you, and so you have the building blocks for a network already to hand. And that hand should be a holding one, the hand of someone ready to hold yours when you are in hospital or perhaps after an accident or a breavement – the phone makes the link, the hand brings the physical contact.

You checklist of qualities could be as follows:

1. Good listening skills.

2. Open-mindedness.

3. Trustworthiness.

4. Give-and-take.

5. Shared fun.

6. Realistic optimism, not doom and gloom depressed soul-mates.

To make a friend start by being a friend by:

1. Taking the initiative.

2. Saying 'thank you'.

HOBBIES AND PLAY

While many adults know how to work they have forgotten to play and enjoy themselves. Both are vital in reducing stress.

The first principle is to do something that you *want* to do — whether it is crochet work or skydiving. Don't just follow the fashion.

Here are some guidelines to help you:

1. Make a list of what makes you feel good. It should also provide some elements that your job or home life lack.

2. Recall how you used to play in your teens and early

twenties — participant or spectator, team or solo games, cooperative or competitive, conventional or unconventional.

3. List the activities you did not like and why you didn't.

4. However busy you are, make time for play.

5. Don't let your hobbies take you over. If they become too serious then the benefit will be lost.

6. Your pastime should engage your interest – being slumped in front of the television does not.

7. Keep an open mind about how far you can push yourself – holding back because you feel you are not up to something loses the advantage of stretching yourself. Working as a volunteer in a home for the elderly can be just as valuable mentally as trying to reach an athletic record.

And in case you cannot think of an activity, go to your local library or adult education centre and look at a list of the enormous range of possibilities open to you.

HOUSEHOLD APPLIANCES

We surround ourselves with modern, electrical gadgets and unless we keep them in their place they can become part of a home jungle of the unexpected and worrying. Thinking that you have forgotten to turn off the gas or the electricity under a pan of milk when you are just about to get on your charter flight for a holiday is a recipe for worry. Without going over the top, it is possible to find gadgets to control your gadgets by looking through those little picture catalogues that seem to come with everything through the letterbox.

Home, Stress-Free Home

To see how to make life easier carry out a stress audit of your home and work surroundings.

193

Some ideas:

1. An automatic shutoff iron, or an adaptor in the wall to do the same.

2. Light switches that go on and off to make the house look occupied, or to turn your stereo on and off, make you feel more secure while you are out.

3. Kitchen timers so that the evening meal can be cooked when you get home, or to stop you burning it while you are having a bath, which you stopped overflowing with a pressure-timer while you were preparing the dinner!

4. Magnetic bottle-opener or other gizmos for quick and simple tasks, kept ready to hand so that you do not have to rummage through a drawer-full of junk in the kitchen.

5. Insulate your pipes and water tanks – it costs very little, needs no expertise and could save you more than worry.

6. Get a pet-flap, and a burglar-proof one, so you do not become your pet's doorman.

7. Even for the garden-hater, chores like winding up an unwindable hose pipe could all be avoided by getting a hose reel.

8. Electric strimmers for getting at all the rubbish parts of your garden not only save backbreaking work but give you the incentive to do it.

9. Magnetic nail holder – holds it in place and saves your thumb from the hammer.

10. Traction mats for mud and snow.

11. Shopping and luggage trolleys are not just for the elderly!

IMAGERY

Try the following. 'Command' your mouth to 'produce and secrete saliva'. It did not work, did it? Now try, as vividly as

194

possible, to picture yourself biting into a lemon and tasting its wetness and sourness. No doubt that produced an effect!

Our autonomic nervous system is linked to our *unconscious* mind. We cannot tell it what to do, but you can communicate with it through images. To raise your heart rate you can think of being attacked by a mugger with a knife on the Underground late at night. To slow it down you can think of sleeping in a hammock in the sun. There are critics of this technique of visualization but among its supporters are many women who found it helped them in childbirth, some cancer sufferers and it even helped Jean-Claude Killy win gold medals.

A Trip to the Land of Relax

Make yourself comfortable. Take about six deep breaths, breathing slowly and deeply to relax your body from toes to scalp. Count down slowly from 10 to zero and feel relaxation spreading through your body.

Now imagine that you are in a peaceful, safe and beautiful place(perhaps somehwere you know) or that you are floating on a cloud. Then try to sense and feel everything around you – trees, blossoms, their scent, the sun, the birds, the smell of the sea and seaweed, and so on.

These meditations, or 'mini-holidays' in your mind, should be done for three to five minutes, a couple of times a day. If you are under stress then increase this to 20 minutes twice a day for three weeks. It also helps the natural healing process if you are ill.

Your Mental Guru

If you feel you cannot cope with a stressful situation then imagine that you have someone or something to talk it over with. It could be a pet, it could be a blooming rose tree, a wise old man or woman. Use the same process of relaxation first in your place of ideal rest and then conjure up your mental guru. When you spell out your problem, the experts say that you are then able to draw on your own resources of wisdom. Keep a diary of these conversations because you will meet the same situation again.

If you do the opposite, and imagine a very stressful situation and then switch in your mind to your place of peace or a guru, you can begin to train yourself to switch over when a real moment of stress occurs.

Learning to manage your perceptions. Grounding them in concepts of health and happiness are sure ways of being healthy and happy.

LAUGHTER

Laughter is probably man's most natural relief mechanism. It provides immediate relief in a difficult situation to 'break the tension'. Doctors such as Steve Allen, son of comedian Steve Allen, reckon that laughter is as good as a massage, a hot bath or exercise, to reduce stress.

Assault with a Friendly Weapon

There are many ways of using laughter to turn the sour into the sweet. One couple, after waiting 20 minutes to be served in a roadside cafe and being ignored by the waitress, turned down their anger by thinking about getting a postcard and writing to her saying: 'Having a nice time. Wish you were here'.

This all goes back to what was said earlier in the book about how you *perceive* the reality rather than the distortion. Try to see the funny side rather than being depressed by minor things.

There is a physical effect from laughter. This seems to be that your muscles tense up and then relax. And this process, when your sides are splitting, leaves you 'weak with laughter' – totally relaxed.

If you have trouble laughing then perhaps it is time not only to hire a funny video but to take some specific steps:

1. When the going gets tough, mentally remind yourself to have fun and just think how crazy life is.

2. Keep a 'silly scrapbook' with funny cartoons, anecdotes and jokes that you have come across. It can also be a useful reference book when you are going out to a party or for after-dinner jokes for a work celebration.

3. Take a regular dose of humour – a video a week really can help.

4. Take a laugh break instead of a coffee break – you can keep a book of jokes or a humorous novel in your desk at work.

5. Make a silliness check at 4.30 in afternoon – did you smile during the day? This is most important for people who work in the professions and have a public face – doctors, nurses, receptionists are just a few whose mood affects others.

6. Arrange to spend time with people who make you laugh – so they can contaminate you.

So, when stress threatens to get the best of you, remember that for every action there is usually an opposite and equal gut reaction – make yours a belly laugh.

LOVE AND ROMANCE

Shakespeare was right: 'The course of true love never did run smooth.' Love means plumbing the depths of despair and reaching the heights of ecstasy. The fact is, you cannot really have the one without the other. The stress that goes with it is part of the process. The passion of wartime or long-distance romances is fuelled by the very frustration that surrounds them. But you have to recognize the time when you have to put a stop to too much frustration and call a halt and change your relationship – otherwise you will do yourself damage. The signs are easy to see when your job is being affected, you get angry with others, when you begin to be angry at not being able to love.

If You're Looking for a Lover, Search for a Friend.

If you are trying to start afresh after a divorce or breaking up, then practical steps will reduce what is certainly never an easy time. You need to make time available to meet others.

■ Don't spend your timing longing for the 'ideal' mate.

■ Start making contacts.

■ Be extra friendly to neighbours and the people you work with. They are your prime source of a new relationship either directly or through introductions.

■ Get involved in activities that you enjoy because there will be others of like mind who may become more than friends, rather than going to discotheques where you really do not know what people are like.

■ Shrug off rejections – they are part of the normal scene. What you need to do is expose yourself to as many opportunities as possible. 'You never know until you try.' And sometimes you will be the rejector.

When you find someone, and it is rare that someone will never feel the pangs of love in their life, you may also lose them and feel the normal pain of that loss. New chapters in your life may open, causing a change in your relationships or a rift. This does not mean that love has 'failed'. But one should not expect that a relationship which provides both partners with joy, nourishment and stimulation will last for ever. Even within successful, and lasting marriages, passion usually ebbs eventually and its place is partly filled by highly rewarding and less stressful companionship – shared understanding, attitudes and interests. In short, intimate friendship.

What Does an Affair Really Mean?

Perhaps the most stressful kind of love is that between two people who are married, but not to each other. This is equally true for romantic infidelity outside any exclusive love relationship. Such affairs usually arise out of a desire for novelty and excitement or a desire to assure ourselves that we are still attractive. Sometimes an individual has an affair as revenge for something his or her mate did, or out of loneliness during long but unavoidable separations. But sometimes an outside affair, or string of them, serves as a painkiller, to make your marriage or equivalent relationship more bearable. It can serve to distract you from, or buffer the stress of, dealing with problems within the primary relationship.

And hard as it may be to believe, an outside affair sometimes has nothing to do with the primary relationship, it may instead serve as a panacea for a generalized sense of tedium or boredom, or as a consolation for some frustration, not in our marriage, but in our work or career.

When tempted by an extramarital affair it can be important to ask how you would feel about your marriage if you were *not* to have an affair. Then you should ask whether it is worth jeopardizing your primary relationship. On the other hand it is perhaps a mistake to assume that because two people really 'love' each other that it is impossible for either of them to have an affair, or desire one, with anyone else.

When the issue has to be considered, you must decide whether there was infidelity, and what it meant. Some people focus too much on the first issue and not on the second. There is a big difference between a one-night stand with someone your partner does not particularly care about, and a continuing relationship with someone they see every day. Basically, if the primary relationship between two people is good, then they will get through the outside affair.

Controlling Jealousy Before it Controls You

If your partner has strayed, it is not easy to see the philosophical aspects of a fling. Mainly, you feel sick, hurt, angry,

199

distraught, confused, betrayed, trapped, paralysed and undeniably stressed. This is because jealousy is not one emotion but a chaotic jumble of painful feelings. The two basic components are a feeling of battered pride and a fear of losing something you value highly.

Therefore you need to temper jealousy and panic from the outset to prevent a bad situation getting worse. Responses may include protecting your ego by berating your partner or attempting to get even, trying to improve your floundering relationship by attempting to improve your appearance, talking things out and so forth. Men are more likely to externalize the cause – to blame the partner or the third party. Women, on the other hand tend to internalize the cause and blame themselves.

To relieve the stress, and prevent your being devastated, you should exorcise the first twinges of suspicion and jealousy before they take you over. Make sure you have good reason, if you do suspect an affair, because seeking constant reassurance from an innocent partner can destroy an otherwise sound relationship.

If your fears prove to be true, then you can either compete and try to win your partner back or accept the situation and wait for it to come to a head, or make the final break yourself.

Establish an Optimal Distance from the Start

Romantic rivals are not the only trigger of jealousy between lovers. You may feel jealous of a mate's interests in friends, people at work or those they share hobbies or sporting activities with. Undue possessiveness can cause stress for both parties – one person fears being abandoned, while the other feels trapped. The more you are like emotional Siamese twins, joined at the heart, the more you will suffer than people who maintain a reasonable distance between themselves. That is one reason why it is important that each side recognizes the need to have some separate friends and interests. They see the separate identity of each other and have far less fear of being abandoned by the him or her. Friends also take some of the emotional pressures off a single partner to supply all the emotional support we need. This is something that you should negotiate early on in a relationship.

MASSAGE

First of all, avoid massages in places that have flashing neon signs. Instead put yourself in the hands of a trained masseuse or masseur who will transform your uptight, knotty body into a completely relaxed puddle of pure bliss.

Swedish massage is the most common method used for stress management. It was developed by Per Henrik Ling as part of medical programme designed to treat disease and it has often been used for bedridden people. That is why some of the strokes are more stimulating than relaxing. All strokes should be made towards the heart, to stimulate the blood supply as well as the lymph glands. This improves oxygenation of the tissues, improves cell nutrition and helps the removal of body toxins. Pain or tension may vanish.

There are five basic strokes though they may be combined with others from other methods:

1. Effleurage is the long gliding stroke that relaxes muscles.

2. Metrassage is a squeezing and kneading of the muscles.

3. Tapotement uses a karate-style chopping stroke, with the masseur or masseuse hacking, tapping or cupping you with the side of the hand or their fingertips. It is infrequently used in relaxation massage.

4. Vibration is produced by rapidly tapping with two fingers at one or a series of spots.

5. Friction is another technique created when a circular or rolling motion is applied to the muscle near the spine and the joints. It also increases circulation but in a more localized way than the other strokes.

These strokes also form the basis of other hands-on therapies such as shiatsu (acupressure) massage, which is a finger-pressure stimulation of acupuncture 'meridians' which Chinese medicine believes correspond to the flow of energy in your body.

What to Expect

A full-body massage generally lasts an hour and takes place on a hard table. And a good massage therapist will, in addition to the massage itself, send you back with homework such as exercises or instructions on how to massage your legs after a run.

You should be naked with a sheet covering the parts of the body that the therapist never touches: genitals and breasts. Even a modest amount of clothing will impede a massage and will require a massage therapist to leave important muscle groups unmassaged. You may also be told to focus your breathing on the parts of your body being massaged, and to relax. This is the time to let go of tension and not to feel rushed. When the massage is over it is often nice to lie still with your eyes closed.

When you have checked out the right place to go to (which has trained therapists) remember to tell them of any injuries or health conditions you may have.

In the UK it is regarded as unethical to recommend therapists but you can find out whether there is a qualified person in your area by sending a stamped, self-addressed envelope to the West London School of Therapeutic Massage, 41A St Luke's Rd, London W11 1DD.(See Reference List)

MUSIC

When David played his harp for troubled King Saul he became one of the first, historically-recorded, music therapists, someone who knew the powers of this universal language.

Modern music therapists categorize tunes either as stimulating or sedating. An Irish jig gets people clapping their hands or tapping their toes. Sedating music has a much slower rhythm, approximately 60 beats per minute, and as regular as your heartbeat at rest. Calming music has been used to reduce pain and distress at the dentists, during childbirth and in coronary care units and migraine clinics. Experts say that music seems to trigger natural opiates in the brain called endorphins and can take you from stress to relaxation in as little as 30 seconds.

Andante for Relaxation

Flute, harp, piano and string ensemble instrumental pieces tend to be more smoothing than vocal ones. Studies also show that not all classical music is relaxing. Look for sonatas and symphonies played *adagio* (at a slow tempo) or *andante* (moderately slow) that approximate to the heart's natural rate at rest.

Some jazz, blues and other traditional music may also bring calmness although surveys show that canned background music irritates a number of people.

There are also available sound cassettes which use other noises such as the sound of the sea or specifically composed pieces to induce relaxation or a state of meditation. Various companies produce them and you should ask in a record or health products shop. (See Reference List, New World Cassettes)

You can gauge how effective the 'sound therapy' is by how much more slowly and deeply that you breathe. However, if you feel a tightness in the back of your neck or solar plexus you are not receiving its benefits.

NATURE

The first rule for enjoying nature is to appreciate what is already around you. You can walk across Westminster Bridge or overlook Sydney Harbour and be moved by what you see.

One study of this effect on the individual suggested that the benefits fell into two categories – health-related, such as mental relaxation, feelings of receptivity and harmony with the environment. The other was aesthetic-transpersonal experiences such as awareness of beauty and the process of change in the natural world, perceptual alertness, personal insight and expanded identity.

Perhaps a key to nature's ability to soothe lies in the simple fact that it transports us away from our chores and demands and worries.

Treatment with Meadows and Clouds

The director of the wilderness programme at the United World College, Montezuma, New Mexico believes that the benefit comes from 'getting in touch with another reality'. It is also a better way to cope with your feelings than using cigarettes, alcohol or drugs.

The theory is that creating a contact with nature restores one's energy and alleviates negative feelings. It slows life down because of the different rhythm, and this makes it easier to work through decisions you have to take and puts time into a new perspective.

Watch the waves crashing onto the beach and think how many centuries the shoreline has taken their pounding. Look at the side of a cliff and see the millions of years of sedimentation deposits. Summer's glories of colour are replaced by the leaves of autumn.

You can also relax by watching a film or looking at a picture of some scene from nature. Compare the effect of watching reports of violence on the news and a nature film in colour. One study has shown that patients recovering from surgery improve faster when they have a window looking out onto a natural rather than an urban landscape.

You can create a few moments of relaxation by looking out of the window onto a garden or a small park. Sunsets and sunrise can be particularly compelling. Going out and standing in the rain will make you feel better. Even looking at an ant

204

speeding across the floor will give you a sense of nature and the place you have in it.

NUTRITION

When we are under stress our bodies use up nutrients faster and less efficiently than they would do ordinarily. At the very time we most need to eat fish or whole wheat pasta we resort to fastfood and chocolate snacks which sabotage our bodies. A poor diet plus poor digestion, linked to an increased demand for nutrients, signals stress.

The first thing to do is to ensure you eat regularly and healthily. Most of us know what that means today and there are plenty of books to show you if you do not. You can also take advice on whether you should boost your vitamin intake. Vitamin B is used up under stress and when you are run down because the body needs it to turn food into fuel, and supply the brain with glucose. With reduced glucose the brain performs poorly according to Dr Charles Tkacz of the North Nassau Mental Health Center in New York. The B vitamins are also important in nerve function. Other effects of vitamin B deficiency are depression, fatigue and confusion and a reduced immune system effectiveness. Foods which are high in vitamin B include liver, kidneys, whole grain, nuts, seeds and beans.

Points to watch but don't overdo it:

1. You may need more vitamin C.

2. You may need more protein and calcium. The body excretes excessive nitrogen in your urine under stress. Protein is needed as a source of amino acids and they produce enzymes important in combating stress. The B vitamins in turn are 'co-enzymes' helping the amino acids do their work. However, instead of overeating you should boost your intake with moderate amounts, at regular intervals over the day, of chicken, fish, eggs and something like peanut butter on wholemeal bread. Of course you can also drink milk and eat low-fat dairy products.

3. You don't need fats or the calories they are full of.

4. You don't need caffeine – it stimulates.

5. You don't need much sugar.

PETS

The four-legged friend is still the best friend in the world. The one certain source of undemanding friendship as you come home from a hard day is the pet who bounds towards you while children are glued to the box and your partner complains over the dinner in the kitchen. Pets are the one source of constancy in our lives and the reason we groom them, hug them, feed them what they like most, baby them and buy them toys is because they give far more than they demand. They not only bring the child out in us but they give us companionship and security; they make us feel calm when we touch them and take us away from the endless world of competition.

There is plenty of evidence today about the importance, physically and psychologically, of keeping a pet. For the elderly they are someone to talk to in their loneliness. The concern for a pet's safety while someone is in hospital proves this. If someone is worried that their pet is not being looked after while they are away, then they are likely to recover less quickly. Take a group of well-mannered dogs into an old folks' home and see how the residents light up and break out of their lethargy.

Pets in childhood also provide unseen benefits. Various studies show that those of us who grew up with pets are more self-reliant, sociable and tolerant. Boys become men with a stronger sense of personal worth and better social skills. Women who were raised with dogs are more flexible and more self-reliant. Cats help children grow into adults with a heightened belief in their personal value to society and more social responsibility. All this means that you can deal with stress better. And flexibility is part of that coping process. It has also been shown that pets, particularly cats, give people a better feel for understanding body language and facial expression and so are able to communicate with others better.

The dog-walker not only has a good excuse to start chatting to another dog-owner, but to make friends. When you stroke their dog and talk to it, it lowers your blood pressure and when you do the same with your own dog it goes even lower.

The evidence also shows that staring at gold fish in a tank at the dentist's will also prepare you better for the drill – it can be as effective as pain hypnosis. You will also have a better chance of surviving a heart attack if you have a pet to go home to after hospitalization. Studies showed that those with pets were more likely to be alive one year later than those without.

But Choose the Proper Pet

If the pet is to relieve your stress then do not choose the wrong one for the wrong environment. A London teacher with a beautiful red-setter had to leave it in the house all day and was not near a park for it to go bounding about. In the end the strain and worry about the poor animal being stuck at home led him to give it to a farmer as a field dog – everyone was happy again. So ask yourself what you need and what the pet will need. If you go for a cat because you are out all day, maybe you need to have two so that they can take their aggression out on each other through play rather than take it out on your furniture or through scratching and spitting.

It really is important to get yourself a book on how to look after your pet. You certainly should not buy your dog on impulse and, if possible, it should come from a reliable breeder not on a whim from a pet shop window. You are going to live with them for 10 to 15 years so it should be done seriously. Looks are not important, temperament is.

POSITIVE THINKING

We have already talked about the need to think positively but a short analysis of this subject on its own will not be out of place here. Rather than being a person who cannot stand the sight of a half-empty glass (pessimists) or a half-full glass (optimists) we should be thinking about how to fill the glass to the top. Nor should you regard life as a series of spilled-milk incidents – feeling on top of things also means getting on top of them and not being mesmerized by problems.

Michael Scheier, Professor of Psychology at Carnegie-Mellon University in Pennsylvania, says that there is a growing body of evidence that, because an optimist anticipates a favourable outcome, they actually are led to do something to make it come out right. This fits in with the concept that we become stressed because we perceive events to be threatening or harmful and reacting positively will reduce that stress. Setbacks at work, in love, in financial matters and so on, should be seen as opportunities for change and growth, not excuses for giving up.

You may have a better chance of handling stress if you transform positive thoughts into positive results by *active* coping:

1. Focus on the problem and plan to solve it quickly.

2. Persevere when others might quit.

3. If you solved the problem once before then it will be easier this time!

4. Optimists remain so because they have learnt to use their social support network.

5. Optimists also know when to accept a situation, resign themselves to it, and then move off on another tack.

If you are a pessimist then things really will become self-fulfilling prophecies – because you let them happen. So pessimists must break the cycle by telling themselves that, although it has always gone wrong in the past, they are going to change things this time.

If you are in doubt as to what kind of person you are, then ask yourself if you are a whiner or a winner. If you are the former you always look on the dark side instead of the bright side. If the latter, you follow medical treatment and succeed in giving up smoking or tackling an obstacle which may appear unsurmountable to pessimists. Look on active coping as a kind of 'survival of the optimistic' in terms of mental evolution – a new aspect of hardiness.

PRAYER AND RELIGION

It has become obvious that many of the things we have been talking about on the relaxation, meditation, love and support front have parallels, or may be derived from traditional elements, in religion and prayer. These elements do not necessarily mean that you have to be committed to some particular doctrine or dogma of a specific church or movement to benefit from them. Religion, rather than a creed, is a much wider manifestation of mankind's search for a role, so your 'God' may differ from others if you wish.

Why Praying Works and Wishing Doesn't

Dr Herbert Benson, who is credited with identifying the Relaxation Response, suggests that 'foxhole' prayers ('Oh God! Don't let me get killed') do not work at all. He says the aim should be a form of meditation, including prayer, combined with a profound set of personal convictions, and this will reduce stress in a number of ways. Prayer relaxes and breaks up a chain of worrying thoughts which may have been producing the cycle of insomnia, indigestion etc, that follows anxiety. If your prayer is rooted in specific religious beliefs, it gives problems a much smaller place in a much bigger global and universal perspective. Remember too that 'religious' belief, of course, may be much stronger in a committed conservationist than in a doctrinal bigot.

This core of beliefs also provides people with strength in times of stress and this is reinforced by the concepts and practices of forgiveness, patience and understanding. It helps you cope with blame, bitterness, discouragement, cynicism and hostility. Obviously, if you feel part of a bigger system of beliefs, of whatever kind, then you know you will never be on your own.

Once again, studies show less ailments and stress among those who pray and meditate regularly. The vegetarian diet of certain religious groups has given them less risk of cancer and heart attack. Israeli doctors, writing in the *International Journal of Cardiology,* have found that Orthodox Religious Jews may be less at risk from such problems because of their very strong social and psychological group support system and their deep conviction in the help of an all-powerful God.

When you pray you should follow the guidelines already spelt out for relaxation and visualization, normally spending 10 to 20 minutes, twice a day, before breakfast and dinner if possible.

RELAXATION RESPONSE

You have come across this a number of times so far and, because it is an important element in stress reduction, we can provide a summary about it here.

The body reacts usually with a fight-or-flight response to events. Just as this is an automatic response, so we need to have an automatic Relaxation Response, the title chosen by Dr Herbert Benson for his book.

Dr Benson, by analysing thousands of years of rituals, came up with the quick method that we have already explained.

What you need to do is remember the benefits so that you convince yourself to carry out the procedure at least once, but preferably twice, a day. This will decrease your overall stress, blood pressure etc, and also enable you to call the Relaxation

Response into action when an unexpected event stresses you at work, at home or in the street – this is what 'staying cool' is all about. You must find and maintain your slot for it somewhere during the day – it could be while travelling to work or when you have got your children off to school.

REST BREAKS

Remember these? Then learn this shortened technique off by heart:

1. Deep breathing, standing with you arms at your sides, inhaling deeply through your nose, filling your lungs from the bottom up while raising your shoulders. Hold for two to three seconds and exhale slowly through your nose and lower your shoulders.

2. Stamina stretches, to reduce fatigue and relax your muscles, are carried out by stretching your arms over your head and pretending you are climbing up a rope. Next, raise both arms high above your head until you can feel your whole body stretching out. Then shrug your shoulders, concentrating on tightening shoulder and upper back muscles and hold this for ten seconds, then let your shoulders drop. Repeat four times. Next,stand or sit erect, looking straight ahead. Slowly turn your head to left and right and then up and back, to look at the ceiling, and then down towards your chest.

3. Arm circles re-oxygenate your blood by standing straight with your arms extended out to the sides. Rotate both arms simultaneously, beginning with small clockwise circles and making bigger and bigger circles totalling ten in all and then repeat counterclockwise.

4. Brain-boosting imagery stimulates your tired brain. Sit down, clear your brain of intrusive thoughts and say to yourself, 'I am feeling strong, alert and refreshed. Every part of me is full of positive energy'.

211

5. Power snacks are to replenish your brain and muscles with fluid – perhaps cold, fizzy mineral water or fruit juice. Before starting work again, just savour the alertness you feel.

6. Security blankets are your way of using 'holding therapy'. If you cannot hug someone you know or the time is wrong, just remember your teddy-bear or favourite childhood toy or model car. Some people keep worry beads to 'hold and feel', or a worry egg. But it may be a pipe or key ring mascot that you can hold on to. Children who are deprived of bodily contact are the ones who show us the value of 'holding' when they are brought out of themselves later in life through this therapy. There have been amazing advances recently in its use with autistic children.

You need to have a safe harbour at home and it can be an activity, not just a room, that retains your attention irrespective of what is going on around you – sticking stamps in an album or sorting your holiday photos into a holder may be just the thing.

SELF-HELP GROUPS

Whether it is Alcoholics Anonymous, or Gingerbread for single parents, there are no end of self-help groups nowadays and there has to be one for you. It is a reflection of the individualism of modern society that there are so many groups catering for different needs. It also an antidote to the corresponding loneliness that individualistic society creates. So joining a group is really all about returning to the old community spirit, but with none of the village bitchiness. Some groups are for those with problems, others are for those who want to meet others and enjoy themselves.

In all instances they provide social support. But their members also benefit from the fact that it is usually better to give than to receive – you get more out of it than you put in. They also help to reinforce your determination to tackle a problem or a solution, offering you role models and usually a method that has been tried before so you do not have to re-invent the wheel. The fact that discussions are diluted in the group means too that the pressure is not directed at you.

If you have never been to such a group then pop along to your library and they will provide you with a list as long as your arm. Then pop along to one that interests you. If you do not like it, try another. First visits may be a little bit awkward because you may feel you are the outsider – that is a test of the group. They should make you feel welcome.

If there is no group for your particular need, then the path of starting your own is well trodden. You may be suffering from some particular and rare problem. Go to a group that already handles something particular to them and ask them how to start your own group up – they will be delighted to help. From then on it is just a question of using your local paper, television or radio station to let people know what you are doing and they will be relieved to get in touch – they were on their own too.

And by the way – professionals such as doctors are no longer as resistant as they were in the past to such movements being started up so don't forget to ask them or call on them for help.

Finally, meetings that are about meetings to decide when to hold meetings are not only a waste of time. They may be stopping you doing something quite new. If something has come to the end of the job that it came into existence to do, then let it die gracefully. As they say, there is no point in flogging a dead horse.

SEX

It's called making love and when all goes well it should provide moments of intense intimacy that not only tune you right up to your maximum but also relax you totally afterwards. There is not enough room here to spell out all the pros and cons that have been written about sex and sexuality. But your sex life

213

should not only be about immense enjoyment. It should also be about caring and tenderness and respect for each other.

Touching is one of the five all important senses and is crucial to our emotional wellbeing. Infants who are not touched can pine and waste away. Sex is also a physical exercise and causes your body to produce its own stimulants and relaxants – that is one reason why you should feel physically better after sex, although it also useful to be aware that men also may feel depressed after the sex act – post-coital depression. There are therapists who suggest that sex also reduces cramps in women because stress is reduced. If you do not feel comfortable putting sex in the same league as a game of tennis then you may be creating stress for yourself instead of reducing it. But you need to feel you are on the same wavelength and have the same perception of sex as your partner, or try to lead each other to a better understanding of how you each see it.

By understanding each other's needs about style, frequency, the right time and the wrong time you will de-stress sex. After all if you have to compromise about the furniture you buy, then you are going to have to compromise on the sex front too.

SLEEP

Sleep is not a waste of a third of your life. It the best remedy for stress and a de-tox process that needs very little to use to the full. You breathe more deeply and slowly, heart and blood pressure levels go down, your metabolism slows up. Your brain pattern during sleep also makes muscles relax. So go back and check through the guidelines we have already given you and put them into practice.

While we are the subject of sleepiness it is also worth learning to stretch when you feel sleepy – cats do it and seem to get great pleasure out of it. So can you. Yawns are one of nature's ways of making us stretch when we forget – so try to anticipate. It helps to flatten out your knotted muscles from

214

too much sitting during the day, just like smoothing out a rumpled woollen sweater.

7

SEEKING PROFESSIONAL TREATMENT

A Consumer's Guide to Pharmaceutical

Stress Reduction

A CONSUMER'S GUIDE TO PHARMACEUTICAL STRESS REDUCTION

There are going to be times when you find that you are unable to cope on a short-term basis with stress and anxiety. This book has tried to alert the reader to spotting danger signs early and taking preventive action. You should not wait till things get too bad before you ask for help. Nor should you rush into someone else's 'medical' or 'psychiatric' arms without being as well informed as possible. This is more important than ever today as one sees the growing concern, and it has been tragically very late in coming, about the number of people who have become very seriously addicted to tranquillisers through overprescribing by doctors and the latter's ignorance and failure to monitor their patients' properly. This blame also has to shared by the producers of certain pharmaceuticals.

There is plenty of blunt talking about this situation today from organizations such as TRANX (UK), the national Tranquilliser Advice Centre (See Reference List). The same goes for CITA, the national Council on Involuntary Tranquilliser Addiction (See Reference List). BBC 1's 'Daytime Live' programme has run a helpline for people addicted this way and one of their experts told viewers that, if they had become addicted, they should make their fears well known to their GP by booking a double appointment and writing their concerns down on a piece of paper so there would be no question of misunderstanding. 'Many doctors are still unaware of the dangers,' they were told. It is important that both doctor and patient decide to tackle the issue positively.

These warnings are even more important for someone who needs to take medication. You should not be put off by the possibility that you may have to take drugs, but you should be in control and in partnership with your doctor. If your doctor is short and sharp, does not show concern, and is not informed about possible addiction, then you really should go to another one or contact TRANX about where you can find a knowledgeable doctor. There is a certain ring of warning in the cynical remark which says that 'Valium is a drug frequently prescribed by doctors to end a consultation.'

Anti-Anxiety Drugs

The benzodiazepines form the majority of minor tranquillisers. This is a list from TRANX (UK).

Chemical/ Generic name	Brand Name	Length of Action	A Anxiolytic H Hypnotic
Alprazolam	Xanax	Medium	A
Bromazepam	Lexotan	Long	A
Chlordiazepoxide	Librium	L	A
*	Limbitrol	L	A
	Tropium	L	A
Clobazam	Frisium	L	A
Clonazepam	Rivotril	Anti-epileptic	A
Clorazepate	Tranxene	L	A
Diazepam	Alupram	L	A
	Atensine	L	A
	Diazemuls	L	A
	Solis	L	A
	Stesolid	L	A
	Tensium	L	A
	Valium	L	A
Flunitrazepam	Rohypnol	L	H
Flurazepam	Dalmane	L	H
Ketazolam	Anxon	L	A
Loprazolam	Dormonoct	M	H
Lorazepam	Almazine	Short	A
	Ativan	S	A
Lormetazepam		M	H
Medazepam	Nobrium	L	A
Midazolam	Hypnovel	Intravenous	A

219

Chemical/ Generic name	Brand Name	Length of Action	A Anxiolytic H Hypnotic
Nitrazepam	Mogadon	L	H
	Nitrados	L	H
	Remnos	L	H
	Somnite	L	H
	Surem	L	H
	Unisomnia	L	H
Oxazepam	Oxanid	S	A
Temazepam	Normison	M	H
Triazolam	Halcion	S	H

*Limbitrol contains Librium and Amitryptiline
(Copyright JJ/Oct. 88)

According to Dr Jacob J. Katzow, associate clinical professor of psychiatry and behavioral science at the George Washington University and Director of the Washington, D.C., Clinic for Mood Disorders, certain tranquillisers are for pure anxiety without significant depression and can reduce stress. Drugs such as flurazepam, temazepam and triazolam can be so relaxing that they are used specifically to treat insomnia.

These drugs work by depressing the central nervous system, but far less than the barbiturates, which is why the benzodiazepines are less dangerous. The routine should be to select the right drug for the right problem in the right amount for the shortest period of time. The benzodiazepines can build up in your body and become toxic; taken with alcohol they can put you to sleep and you may not wake up. You can become physically and/or physiologically dependent on them.

The short-life drugs such as triazolam and oxazepam have a short half-life – on the average your body will use up half the dosage of triazolam in two to four hours, and half the dosage of oxazepam in four to eight hours. When used for insomnia there should therefore be no after-effect in the morning. But remember too, that we are all different and therefore you and your doctor need to fine tune drugs to your particular metabolism. In contrast, something like flurazepam, which is

220

a powerful sleep-inducer, has a half-life of 47 to 100 hours. The older you are, the less your body can excrete the drugs. Diazepam has a half-life of 20 hours in a 20–year-old but a half-life of 90 hours in an eighty-year-old. Various drugs have side-effects which you should ask about, such as nausea, or loss of memory.

Beta-blockers, particularly propranolol, are used to treat anxiety attacks. They block certain nerve impulses to the heart, in effect anaesthetizing it. One advantage is that their half-life is very short – only four hours – and the drug should be completely cleared from the system by the time the anxiety-causing situation has passed. Since they lower the heart rate and blood pressure, they can change the way your body responds to exercise. So if you are put on these you should ask whether you should change any of your daily activities.

There are also drugs for deep depression. The general evidence is that they require a great deal of care in the prescription and in their use. They have a long list of possible side-effects (the anti-anxiety drugs are not free of these either) and the ultimate aim should be to work out a scheme which minimizes or has no recourse to medication at all.

In any case some of the following tips may help you to be sensible with your medication:

■ Try the drug on a weekend at first when you do not have to drive or face work. You can tell your doctor about any side effects.

■ Watch out for signs of dependency – feeling you need to take more and more or feeling that you cannot do without them.

■ Toxic buildup. This can show through poor muscular coordination, agitation, and slurred speech. The disorientation and confusion that can arise may wrongly be diagnosed as senile demntia, so friends of the elderly should be ready to make sure that, in the case of such a diagnosis, no drugs are indirectly involved.

You can always get expert counselling advice, starting either with helplines or self-help groups. Organizations for the addicted such as TRANX (UK) know what it is all about and that is because their telephone counsellors, for example, are all former addicts to medicines. Its founder Joan Jerome is such a person. So they not only know how to help you get off, but to help you avoid starting, by pointing you to alternatives. Quite often root problems need to be identified before trying to take short cuts through medication. The TRANX (UK) newsletter (£1) is an amazing, monthly account by different people, not only of how they have coped with withdrawal, but how they fight back and handle stress. It is a form of positive medication in itself.

The following is reprinted courtesy of their Newsletter and it is offered here because it sums up everything that this book has been about.

I think that I'm cracking up, that I won't cope much longer, but I keep going. I do keep a sense of humour, I can still laugh. You should see Nikki (my dog) when I switch on my relaxation tape, he appears from nowhere, and lies by my side, flat on his back. I kill myself laughing – that's relaxation for you. I've never known a dog so human, and he has so much love. He's super! I thank god for Nikki.

Your Newsletters are my survival kit. I'll never dispose of them. They will have a special place in my treasure chest.

From M.H., Gosport.
Reproduced courtesy TRANX (UK)

KEEPING A STRESS DIARY

A diary can often reveal clues to the causes of stress-related illness, such as headaches, backaches, stomach troubles, colds and flu. To help determine if a persistent but unexplained health complaint is related to stress, keep a brief diary of how you're feeling and what stresses you are coping with on a week-to-week basis.

In column one, fill in the dates, starting with week 1. In column two, jot down your symptoms, and in column three, briefly list any problems you may be having with work, deadlines, children, spouse, finances or other stressful demands. In time, you should be able to see any connection between health and stressful events.

WEEK	SYMPTOMS	STRESSFUL EVENTS

1

....

....

....

2 ....

....

....

....

3 ....

....

....

....

4 ....

....

....

....

5 ....

....

....

....

6 ....

....

....

....

WEEK   SYMPTOMS   STRESSFUL EVENTS

7
....
....
....

8
....
....
....

9
....
....
....

10
....
....
....

11
....
....
....

12
....
....
....

WEEK	SYMPTOMS	STRESSFUL EVENTS

13

14

15

16

17

18

19

....
....
....
....
20
....
....
....
....
21
....
....
....
....
22
....
....
....
....
23
....
....
....
....
24
....
....
....
....

WEEK   *SYMPTOMS*   *STRESSFUL EVENTS*

25

26

27

28

29

30

31

....
....
....
....

32

....
....
....
....

33

....
....
....
....

34

....
....
....
....

35

....
....
....
....

36

....
....
....
....

37

....
....
....
38 ....
....
....
....
39 ....
....
....
....
40 ....
....
....
....
41 ....
....
....
....
42 ....
....
....
....
....

WEEK	SYMPTOMS	STRESSFUL EVENTS

43

....
....
....
....

44

....
....
....
....

45

....
....
....
....

46

....
....
....
....

47

....
....
....
....

48

....
....
....
....

WEEK	SYMPTOMS	STRESSFUL EVENTS

49

....
....
....

50

....
....
....

51

....
....
....

52

....
....
....
....

REFERENCE LIST

Cross referenced by organization and topic.

Action on Stress at Work, brochure from the Health Education Authority, Hamilton House, Mabledon Place, London WC1H 9TX. Tel. 01 631 0930

Action on Smoking and Health (ASH), 5–11 Mortimer Street W1. Tel. 01 637 9843

Addiction to medicines: see Tranquilliser Addiction.

Age Concern, Look in the phone book for your local branch or contact 60 Pitcairn Rd, Mitcham, Surrey CR4 3LL.

Alcoholics Anonymous. Look in the phone book for your local branch or contact Headquarters at PO Box 1, Stonebow House, York Y01 2NJ. Tel. 0904 644026

Audio Ltd, 26–28 Wendell Road, London W12 9RT. Tel. 01 743 1518/4352

Back Pain Association (National). Look in the phone book for your local branch or contact the Headquarters at 31–33 Park Road, Teddington, Middx, TW11 0AB. Tel. 01 977 5474

Bereavement – see Cruse.

Biofeedback:
See Audio Ltd.
Expanding Horizons, Derbyshire House, Crank Road, St Helen's WA11 8RJ. Tel. 0744 895 645

Carers (National Association of), 26 Chilworth Mews, London W2 3RG. Tel. 01 724 7776

Cruse – Bereavement Care. Look in the phone book for your local branch or contact the Headquarters at Cruse House, 126 Sheen Rd, Richmond, Surrey TW9 1UR. Tel. 01 940 4818. A wide range of brochures and supportive information available.

Divorce:
Family Welfare Association.
Look in the phone book for your local branch or contact Headquarters at 501, Kingsland Road, E8. Tel. 01 254 6251. Covers all stress issues affecting individual and for family.

National Family Conciliation Council. Look in the phone book for your local branch or contact Headquarters at 34 Milton Rd, Swindon, Wiltshire, SN1 5JA. Tel. 0793 618486. Has useful information material on the stress of divorce and how to handle it.

Marriage Guidance Council (National) – see RELATE
Elderly — see Help the Aged, Age Concern, Carers.

Gingerbread for Lone Parents and Children. Look in the phone book for your local branch or contact Headquarters at 35 Wellington St, London WC2E 7BN. Tel. 01 240 0953.

Green Cars, 35 Cardozo Road, London N7 9RJ. Tel. 01 607 1996

Help the Aged. Look in your phone book for your local branch or contact Headquarters at St James' Walk, London EC1R 0BE. Tel 01 253 0253, Fax 01 895 1407. Leaflets on issues that concern the wellbeing and safety of the elderly.

Hospital:
National Association for the Welfare of Children in Hospital (NAWCH), Argyle House, 29–31 Euston Rd, London NW1. Tel. 01 833 2041. Offices also at 94 Murrayfield Gardens, Edinburgh EH12 6DJ, Tel. 031 337 6412, and 33 Dilwyn Rd, Sketty, Swansea SA2 9JT, Tel. 0792 202046. Helpful advice and information for parents.

Patients Association – see below

Going into Hospital: A brief guide published by the College of Health (£2.00), 18 Victoria Park Square, Bethnal Green, London E2 9PF.

Hypnotherapy: Contact the Institute for Complementary Medicine.

Institute for Complementary Medicine, 21 Portland Place, London W1N 3AF. Tel. 01 636 9543. £1.50 for a list of organizations.

Living Skills – An Answer to Stress at Work. Teaching pack from the SE Thames Regional Health Authority for use in industry, education, health and social services sectors. £45 from Isabel Smith, Thrift House, Bexhill-on-Sea, East Sussex TN39 3NQ. Tel. 0424 730073, Fax 0424 730249

Look After Yourself! A health programme information pack that includes anti-stress advice particularly on heart disease. From the Health Education Authority, Hamilton House, Mabledon Place, London WC1H 9TX. Tel. 01 631 0930

Management courses for stress: Information from Institute for Complementary Medicine

Marriage Guidance Council (National) – see RELATE

Massage: Send an s.a.e. to The West London School of Therapeutic Massage, 41A St Luke's Rd, London, W11 1DD. Tel. 01 229 4672

Mental Health at Work. Small brochure outlining general principles with contact addresses for further information. The Health and Safety Executive, Information Service, St Hugh's House, Stanley Precinct, Trinity Rd, Bootle, Merseyside L20 3QY. Tel. 051 951 4381. Offices also at Broad Lane, Sheffield S3 7HQ. Tel. 0742 752539 and Baynards House, 1 Chepstow Place, Westbourne Grove, London W2 4TF. Tel. 01 221 0870

Migraine:

Chelsea Physic Garden, Royal Hospital Rd, London SW3
Princess Margaret Migraine Clinic, Charing Cross Hospital, Fulham Palace Road, London W6 8RF. Tel:01 741 7833

The Migraine Trust, 45 Great Ormond Street, London WC1N 3HD. Tel. 01 278 2676

National Council for Voluntary Organisations (NCVO), 26 Bedford Square, London WC1 3HU. Tel. 01 636 4066. Directory of organizations available, £8.95 including postage.

New World Cassettes, Patients Association (The), Room 33, Charing Cross Rd, London WC2H OHR. Tel. 01 240 0671. Self-help directory of national organizations for various diseases and handicaps (£3 including postage). Brochures on self-help and the patient, changing your doctor etc. Send an s.a.e. for details and prices.

Phobias: Contact Patients Association

RELATE (National Marriage Guidance Council). Look in your phone book for your local branch or contact the Headquarters at Herbert Gray College, Little Church St, Rugby CV21 3AP. Tel. 0788 73241. A range of books, booklets and courses covering the home, problems at work, sexuality. The network of local offices offers advice with complete confidentiality. There are brochures for people interested in becoming counsellors.

Self-help groups – contact Patients Association. Also the National Council for Voluntary Organisations.

Smoking: See Action on Smoking and Health.

Superimmunity – Control your Emotions and Improve your Health, Dr Paul Pearsall, Ed. Peter D O'Neill, Ebury Press, London 1988.

Tranquilliser addiction: TRANX (UK), 25a Masons Avenue, Wealdstone, Harrow, Middlesex HA3 5AH. Tel. 01 427 2065 or 01 427 2827 (24 hour answering machine).

Workplace:See: Action on Stress at Work, Mental Health at Work, Living Skills – An Answer to Stress at Work.

INDEX